Introduction to Cell Physiology

The Macmillan Biology Series
General Editors: Norman H. Giles *and* John G. Torrey

INTRODUCTION TO CELL PHYSIOLOGY:
Information and Control

by JOHN L. HOWLAND
Bowdoin College

54299

The Macmillan Company, New York
Collier-Macmillan Limited, London

To Cynthia

First Printing

Library of Congress catalog card number: 68–10127

THE MACMILLAN COMPANY, NEW YORK
COLLIER-MACMILLAN CANADA, LTD., TORONTO, ONTARIO

PRINTED IN THE UNITED STATES OF AMERICA

Preface

The revolution in biology which has occurred during the last decade is due in large part to the application of information theory to biological problems. Biologists have suddenly found at their disposal numerical computers of great power and have hastened to use them in a large variety of applications. More importantly, the point of view of information theory is being accepted by biologists, and the rapid advances in molecular genetics and in the study of the central nervous system have been greatly influenced by analogies between artificial information storage and retrieval devices (such as computers) and living systems.

With the exception of cytogenetics, the field of cell biology has remained relatively free from the outlook of information theory. It has been suggested that cell biology is still engaged in absorbing the full implications of the chemical approach, and until this approach is completely assimilated, additional illumination from new directions will be slow and even somewhat unwelcome. In any case, many of the interesting problems concerning the cell, rather than being matters of molecular properties only, are turning out to be questions of organization—which is to say, information.

For example, there was once a tendency among some physiologists and biochemists to regard the cell as a bag of enzymes. This model is obviously inadequate and certainly unsubtle, but it is inadequate not because cells are not sacks of enzymes, but rather because the enzymes within the sack are organized in an extremely specific way with respect to each other and because their activities are controlled very tightly with respect to the requirements of the cell. In other words, the cell must not only be able to synthesize cell parts but must "know" something about their spatial and temporal organization. This "knowledge" is identical to information in the strict sense of the word. Thus, the control mechanisms of cells do not appear to differ in any important way from those which have already been examined in great mathematical rigor by students of cybernetics.

The purpose of this textbook is to introduce modern cell physiology from the point of view of information and control. Since the field has not reached the state where a rigorous development of physiology from a few information theory postulates is possible (or desirable), the book adopts a fairly conventional organization, with emphasis (harping, one might say) on matters of information and regulation, which are rapidly becoming inevitable in the study of the cell.

In addition, it is the writer's opinion that cell physiology should play a special synthetic role in biology, bringing together results from such areas as cell morphology, biochemistry, and biophysics into a single context, that of the life of the whole, intact cell. Cell physiology brings about an integration of subcellular research into a whole that is truly biology in the sense that only the whole cell is really alive (made up, as we are told, of dead molecules). The purpose of this book is to illustrate the unity of the different areas of cell physiology by emphasizing cellular control mechanisms. The synthesis is aided by the fact that the same sorts of control frequently apply to various otherwise unrelated processes.

It should be added that the book includes a number of aspects not always included in such a text, but which are of considerable importance in the practice of cell physiology. These are discussions of cell compartmentation, enzyme induction and repression, metabolic control mechanisms including respiratory control, and a fairly complete description of the kinetics and control of growth.

The book is addressed primarily to intermediate biology students taking a course in cell or "general" physiology. It presupposes knowledge of introductory chemistry as well as a desire to examine the cell in the full light of its integration and subtlety.

In the writing of this book, I was greatly assisted by numerous colleagues and students. Most especially, I would like to express my appreciation to Professor S. S. Butcher and Professor C. E. Huntington of Bowdoin College, both of whom were exceedingly generous with their time and a great deal of constructive advice. Finally, the conscientious assistance of Mrs. V. Richardson in the preparation of the manuscript is gratefully acknowledged.

J. L. H.

Contents

CHAPTER 1

Cell Organization

There was a time when it was fashionable to divide biological disciplines into morphology and function. That is, cell structure was what cells looked like and cell function was what they did. More recently, it has become clear that cell morphology must be extended to greater and greater detail and magnification, so that a cell morphologist is involved with molecules themselves. In other words, there is no real difference between the examination of gross cell structure and the fine structure of protein molecules, except in the matter of technique. However, when one begins to look at anatomy on the molecular scale, the distinction between structure and function becomes extremely unclear and one always ends up deeply involved in both.

This book will therefore proceed as if there were no line between cell morphology and activity, as in fact there is not. It is, however, necessary to begin somewhere, and a definition and brief description of the cell follows. The definition is really what is called the *cell theory*, which, in turn, is really the history of cell study. Cell theory is little more than the observation that organisms tend to be made up of smaller, closed units, which were called *cells* by Robert Hooke in 1665, by analogy to the rooms in a nunnery. Hooke had, in fact, only seen the holes in cork where cells had been, but the name remains to describe the basic units of

biological organization. About two centuries went by before microscopists recognized that the contents of the holes were interesting. In
the period from about 1830 to about 1900, the contents of cells came
into the light and such objects as nuclei and mitochondria were described in astonishing details as general cell components. Obviously the
observations of cells, which tend to be quite small, was limited for many
years by the low resolution of the optical devices available. Important
advances in microscopy, such as the construction of modern high-
magnification light microscopes and the development of electron optics,
have produced rapid progress in cell study, and the end is certainly not
in sight.

Models of cell structure

The ability to view the interior of the cell in increasingly fine detail
has led to a succession of models describing the character of cells. The
fact that these were models and not final and definitive views of cell
structure is much more obvious in retrospect than when the various
models were described. For example, Hooke's formulation of a model
for cell structure was that cells were hollow rooms, a version not
particularly consistent with modern electron microscopy, but quite in
keeping with Hooke's own observations.

Hooke's model was abandoned in the 1800s for the more complicated
description of a cell as a closed sack containing a fairly liquid material
(*cytoplasm*) in which float fairly solid objects (*organelles*). This was (and
is) consistent with all observations possible in the pre-electron-microscope
era and is at present the point of view of almost any layman who knows
what a cell is. The sack-of-organelles model is quite satisfactory in many
ways and tends to guide one in many of the procedures of analytical
cytology described later in this chapter.

A number of refinements on the sack-of-organelles model became
possible, based on advances in other fields. For example, the first half
of the present century saw the rise and decline of cell models based on
studies of colloidal phases of matter. Colloidal systems are composed of
stable suspensions of small particles, which, owing to size, charge, and
great total surface, possess unusual properties of viscosity and stability.
A classical example of a colloidal system is the protein, gelatin, which
has looked to a number of people not unlike the material within a cell.
Since cell material has been known for a long time to contain consider-

able protein, and since certain cell features are reminiscent of colloidal properties, much effort has been directed to the study of the cell as a colloidal system. However, the development of electron microscopy as well as modern protein chemistry has sent the colloid model into eclipse, because examination of protoplasm at high magnification reveals, not a colloidal suspension nearly as much as a complex mass of infolded membranes of a high degree of order and often considerable beauty. It is probably fair to say that "the colloid character of protoplasm" is no longer taken seriously by workers in the field, in that it no longer serves as the basis for experiments or assists in the interpretation of observations but lives on only in textbooks, where, unfortunately, it is not always presented as history.

Cell organelles

Contemporary views of cell structure emphasize the close interrelations between parts, so that it has been impossible, for a number of years, to think of organelles as floating free in a homogeneous cytoplasm. Organelles should be viewed not so much as subcellular organs, complete in themselves, but as characteristic configurations of cytoplasm, usually involving membranes, which appear in a variety of cells investigated.

For example, the *nucleus*, while appearing in the light microscope to be a closed entity having little structural relationship with the surrounding cytoplasm, is in fact neither completely closed nor entirely a distinct entity. The double nuclear membrane is seen in electron micrographs to have distinct openings, so that the *nucleoplasm* within is in some form of communication with the cytoplasm without, and the membrane may appear continuous with other membranes of the cell (Figures 1–1 and 1–3). The nucleus under high resolution has a granular appearance and contains one or more coarsely granular objects called *nucleoli*, which are not bounded by membranes. The nucleus is known to have a high concentration of *deoxyribonucleic acid* (DNA), which probably represents the granularity. On the other hand, the nucleolus contains *ribonucleic acid* (RNA), so that the entry into the cell of the enzyme ribonuclease, which hydrolyzes RNA, leads to dissolution of nucleolar structure.

In the case of cells of higher organisms, division of the cell is preceded by the aggregation of DNA-containing nuclear material (*chromatin*) into compact bodies, the *chromosomes*. The aggregation into chromosomes represents a mechanism whereby equal partition of genetic

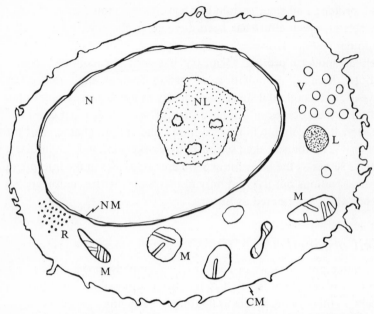

Figure 1–1. *Diagram of an animal cell. This drawing is based on a composite of several electron micrographs of cultured human kidney cells taken by Dr. Micheline M. Mathews. Representative structures are denoted as follows: N—nucleus, NL—nucleolus, NM—nuclear membrane, M—mitochondria, L—lysosome, V—vacuoles, R—ribosomes (in this case, not shown as associated with the endoplasmic reticulum), and CM— the cell membrane. Note the complexity of the cell membrane.*

material (DNA) into two daughter cells is assured. After cell division is completed, the DNA is again distributed evenly throughout the nucleus, an arrangement which allows a maximum surface for the information transfer involved in protein synthesis.

Within the cytoplasm, the nonnuclear part of the cell, are seen a number of small objects which, with electron microscopy, turn out to be highly organized membranous entities. Of these, the *mitochondria* are prominent in number and design. Mitochondria are found in all aerobic higher cells and are involved in energy-transfer processes resulting from respiration. An animal cell might contain on the order of 1,000 mitochondria. They consist of a closed outer membrane and an inner membrane folded to form cristae, providing an increase in available surface. Since many of the processes of mitochondria take place on or in the membrane, the increased surface provides a greater number of sites of action and greater activity per mitochondrion. Very high resolution electron micrographs show the inner membrane to bear small knobs situated on short stalks. The knobs are said to be the loci of energy transfer reactions, leading to the synthesis of the "high-energy" compound adenosine triphosphate, ATP (see Chapter 6).

Another cytoplasmic organelle bounded by a closed membrane is the *lysosome*, which appears to contain enzymes which scavenge dead cells and cell parts. Lysosomes, within their relatively uncomplicated membrane, contain a homogeneous material which is certainly protein, and probably largely proteolytic enzymes (which hydrolyze protein), together with other enzymes which break down cell components, including ribonuclease, deoxyribonuclease, and phosphatases. Presumably, the role of the lysosomal membrane is to separate the lytic enzymes from the rest of the cell to avoid destruction of the components of the viable cell. When the cell becomes moribund, the membrane is thought to break down and release the lysosomal enzymes, which then clean things up.

Photosynthetic plant cells invariably contain chloroplasts, in which are located the photosynthetic pigments and numerous enzymes involved in photosynthetic energy production and carbon assimilation. Although the exact form of chloroplasts is quite variable, especially as one compares flowering plants with the algae, in general the chloroplast is built up of layers of parallel membranes upon which the photosynthetic pigments, such as chlorophyll, are located. In many cases there exists regions within the chloroplast where membranes are more closely applied than elsewhere, and such regions are termed *grana*, after their grain-like appearance in the light microscope. The whole chloroplast is bounded by a closed membrane.

Recent studies point to the idea that chloroplasts (and also mitochondria) possess a high degree of autonomy in the cell—they are self-propagating structures. Since they seem to preside in their own synthesis, it is not surprising that both chloroplasts and mitochondria have been shown to contain significant amounts of DNA, which is known to be the genetic material. The ability of mitochondria to make more mitochondria is also reflected in active protein synthesis in purified preparations.

Much of the cytoplasm in higher organisms is filled with an intricate array of membranes, collectively called the *endoplasmic reticulum*. The endoplasmic reticulum is continuous with the nuclear membrane as well as with the outer (plasma) membrane of the cell. In some regions of some cells the endoplasmic reticulum takes on a tubular appearance which may be seen with the light microscope; the reticulum is then called the *Golgi apparatus*. Much of the endoplasmic reticulum is covered with small bodies called *ribosomes*, which are the sites of much or most of the protein synthesis of cells and which are about 50 per cent RNA. Regions where the reticulum is covered with ribosomes are called *rough endoplasmic reticulum*; those which lack ribosomes are called *smooth*. It is also possible to find regions where ribosomes exist without the membranes. Clear electron micrographs of many cells show extremely compact and convoluted membranes filling most of the cytoplasm and carrying the other organelles of the cell in their interstices. The vision of cells packed full of membranes contrasts strongly with models of cell structure based on a simple, homogeneous cytoplasm.

On the other hand, the compact and orderly membrane systems of the cytoplasm represent something of a problem, in that they suggest that movement within the cytoplasm is unlikely. Unlikely or not, anyone who has seen time-lapse motion pictures of living cells must be struck with the confusion of activity and motion that occurs there. The cytoplasm streams about the cell carrying organelles and leaving one with an impression hard to reconcile with that obtained from static electron micrographs. This represents one of many instances where results obtained with a single method of cell study appear very incomplete in themselves and must be held in balance with those from other techniques.

Many cells are able to propel themselves through a liquid medium or, if stationary, to move the medium across their surface. In most instances this is accomplished by the action of cilia (short) or flagella (longer). With the single (and important) exception of bacterial cells, cilia and flagella are built on a universal pattern where the structure originates in a basal granule within the cytoplasm. In cross section, cilia and flagella are seen to be founded by a sheath which contains an array of nine double, hollow fibers with an additional pair on the center (Figure 1–2). It is interesting that the distinctive ninefold symmetry is present in the centriole, which is found in animal cells only and is involved in cell division.

Bacterial flagella present an entirely different appearance, being much smaller (about one tenth of the diameter of plant or animal flagella) and of much simpler structure. Instead of the ninefold symmetry, the bacterial flagellum appears to be composed of a single fibrous protein

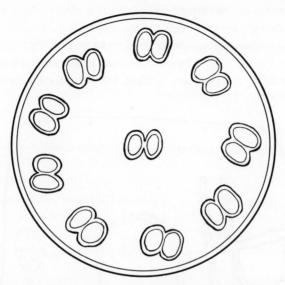

Figure 1–2. *Illustration of the nine-fold symmetry observed in a cilium or flagellum. The 9 + 2 tubules are bounded by an outer double membrane, an arrangement also characteristic of the animal centriole.*

molecule, often with a characteristic periodicity. The fundamental difference between bacterial flagella, on one hand, and those of all higher cells, on the other, is important evidence that bacteria represent something apart from the two kingdoms of classical phylogeny.

Cell membrane topology

It is well known that the surface of a sphere divides all space into two components, inside and outside. Cells are often thought of as somewhat deformed spheres, with the world on one side of their closed cell membrane and cell contents on the other. Thus all points within the cell would be separated from all points without by the cell membrane, and for a molecule (such as food) to pass from the outside to the interior, it would have to traverse the cell membrane. The same view might apply to the nucleus, whose membrane would divide space into nucleus and the world (which would include the rest of the cell). Such ideas about cell topology, however, are not consistent with many observations that have been made.

The continuity of the endoplasmic reticulum with the cell membrane means that the exterior of the cell pushes deep into the cytoplasm and, in fact, is also intimately connected with the region just around the nucleus (see Figure 1–3). Thus the distinction between the inside and outside of a cell is not particularly clear, but it is safe to say that many

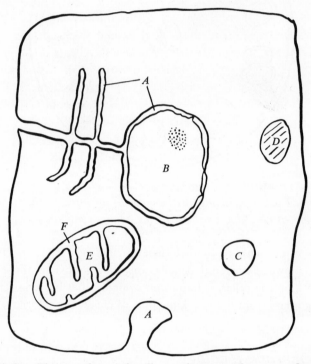

Figure 1–3. *The topology of cell membranes. This very diagramatic rendition of a cell illustrates some of the spaces defined by membranous structures. A may be thought of as the exterior, even when it penetrates deeply. B is the nuclear space, C that within a vacuole, D that within a lysosome. E is the intramitochondrial space, while F is between the outer and inner mitochondrial membranes and penetrates into the cristae.*

regions of cells quite far from the periphery are in close contact, none-theless, with the exterior. Such a conclusion is obviously quite important with reference to the permeation of molecules to and from the cell itself.

The remarks that have been made about cell structure in the preceding paragraphs are all of a general character, and it must be added that the details of cell structure are extremely rich, with great variation between cells of different organisms and within a single organism. The structure of a given cell must always be related to the particular function of that cell and its place in the evolutionary scheme. For example, bacterial cells, as well as those of blue-green algae, present a picture almost totally unlike that of a mammalian liver cell. They lack such organelles as mitochondria, lysosomes, and a defined nucleus with a membrane around it. Those bacteria that are photosynthetic are without chloroplasts, usually containing much simpler and much smaller spherical chromatophores, and motile bacteria have flagella very different from those of a higher organism. Such wild variation in cell structure discourages one from making universally applicable statements about the structure of the cell and encourages electron microscopists to examine a wider array of organisms. Electron microscopy (like many areas of modern biology) has been concerned with a relatively small sampling of the total number of organisms extant, and much is yet to be learned from an increasingly comparative approach.

The internal liquid environment of the cell

The chemical and physical activities that take place within the cell occur either at the protein-lipid membranes or, in solution, in the aqueous spaces within them. To understand the events that occur in solution, it is useful to consider some of the properties of water as a solvent, especially as they apply to the cellular scale of events.

For example, it is well known that water is an unusually good solvent, dissolving not only salts, but many nonionizable organic molecules as well. Water also has an unusually high heat capacity, which means that considerable heat must be added to a sample of water to raise the temperature. This property enables water to serve as a sort of temperature buffer on both a cellular and environmental scale. Water also shows a high dielectric constant, a property which promotes formation of ion pairs of solutes. All these aspects of water chemistry are related, at least in part, to the fact that the water molecule is very polar—there is a large separation of the charge within the molecule.

A water molecule might be said to consist of a center of net negative charge (the oxygen atom) and two relatively positive hydrogens. The separated charges on the water molecule tend to attract nearby ions of opposite charge, thus stabilizing the dissociated form of the ion pair. The ion (or a charged molecule) should be pictured as surrounded by a shell of water molecules held by their oppositely charged ends.

In addition, water molecules tend to associate with each other in a consistent fashion. The crystal structure of ice (see Figure 1–4) represents the associative properties of water when thermal motion is at a minimum. The fact that water has a high heat of melting reflects the fact that the bonds that hold the crystal lattice together are so strong that considerable energy is required to break them.

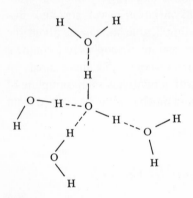

Figure 1–4. *Geometry of water molecules in ice. Dashed lines represent hydrogen bonds.*

The sort of bonding that holds ice together also occurs in liquid water, although the degree of order is much less. Liquid water should be thought of as containing many centers of transient aggregation, with too short a life to give a rigid structure. The forces of attraction are examples of hydrogen bonding, a more general type of interaction between hydrogen and a relatively negative center, such as an oxygen atom. A hydrogen bond exists in addition to a covalent bond and is of a lower order of bond energy. Such bonds exist not only between different molecules, but within a single molecule; many of the unique properties of proteins and nucleic acids reflect intramolecular hydrogen bonds. By virtue of hydrogen bonding, water in the vicinity of a cellular membrane (which will be seen to have many charged centers) is thought to form a highly oriented layer, often a number of molecules thick. The formation of a sort of "ice" in the region of a membrane cannot fail to influence reactions and events that take place in or on the membrane surface.

Not only does water promote the formation of ion pairs in other molecules, but it forms them itself. The dissociation actually involves two molecules of water and leads to the production of ions according to the equation

$$2HOH \rightleftharpoons H_3O^+ + OH^-$$

The fact that this reaction occurs, as opposed to a simple unimolecular dissociation into H^+ and OH^-, indicates that there is a high degree of association between separate molecules and that the proton is quite mobile, so that the exchange may take place as shown in Figure 1–5.

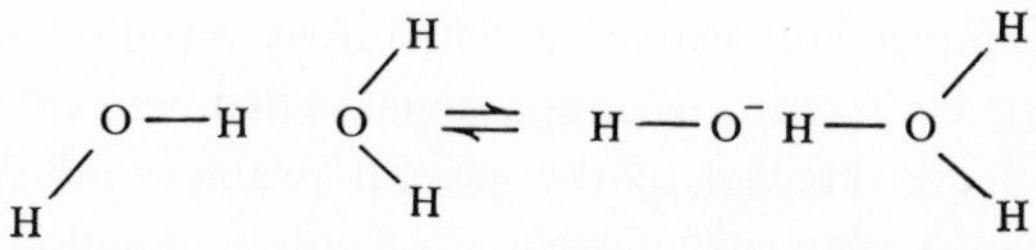

Figure 1–5.   *Formation of* H_3O^+ *and* OH^- *in water.*

Since it was once believed that the dissociation of water was a simple unimolecular process, yielding H^+ and OH^-, it is quite common to refer to the hydrogen ion content of water when H_3O^+ is the actual species. In fact, this represents no real difficulty, as H_3O^+ is itself a good proton donor and a dissociable water molecule may be regarded as a weak acid. For this reason, H_3O^+ and H^+ may be used interchangeably.

Since water is capable of ion formation and since many of the cell components form ions in the aqueous part of the cell, the degree of ionization of such compounds and the related H^+ (and H_3O^+) concentration of the cell are of considerable interest to the physiologist. Since the actual degree of ionization of water is quite small (the concentration of H_3O^+ in pure water is about $10^{-7}M$), an exponential scale for such concentration has been devised, according to which H_3O^+ concentration is expressed as pH:

$$pH = -\log_{10} [H_3O^+]$$

Since many molecules in cells are directly affected by the pH of their medium (see Chapter 3), the cell biologist is often concerned to discover the actual pH of the cell interior, a task to which very ingenious experiments have been put.

The techniques, which include the insertion of microelectrodes as well as pH-indicating dyes into cells, have led to the conclusion that cells are normally poised slightly on the acid side of neutrality. It goes without saying that the insertion of electrodes and dyes into cells produces changes in the cells being studied and does not necessarily give information which is valid for undisturbed cells. Recently the dye approach to cell pH has been used to determine the internal pH of a cell organelle, the mitochondrion, a matter seen in Chapter 8 to have an important bearing on the role of mitochondria in energy transfer and membrane transport.

Techniques of analytical cytology

Although many techniques for cell study are available, and new ones are being developed and exploited with great rapidity, we shall be concerned here with only two approaches which are of central importance. Both are directed to the general problem of correlating a cellular event (such as an enzymic reaction) with the fraction of the total cell structure involved.

An important area of technique is the powerful one of cytochemistry, where an event is localized microscopically in a cell by means of its ability to produce a visible alteration in the color of a dye. For example, a number of dyes are able to react with cellular oxidative enzymes, producing a change in the oxidation-reduction state of the dye molecule and a consequent change in its color. Thus the dye "stains" for the presence of the enzyme with which it reacts, and serves to locate that enzyme in a sectioned cell. Cytochemistry has yielded important results of this sort, and has frequently provided good correlation with results obtained in other ways. The chief limitation of the method has been the difficulty of demonstrating unambiguously that the dyes really react only with the right enzyme, under conditions of cytological staining.

A second approach to the relationship between cell events and cell structure has been the physical separation of cells into their "subcellular" components. Thus cells may be disrupted and fractionated into readily identifiable parts, including fairly pure nuclei, mitochondria, ribosomes, and other organelles (see Figure 1–6). Disruption may be brought about by grinding tissue with an abrasive such as alumina or frozen carbon dioxide, by application of high-energy sound, or by extrusion at high pressure through a small orifice. Selection and careful use of the most appropriate method results in destruction of the cell membrane and liberation of reasonably intact organelles. One may then separate the organelles by differential centrifugation, where low-speed centrifugation sediments the larger organelles (such as nuclei), while progressively greater forces are required for sedimentation of smaller ones (such as mitochondria and ribosomes). After centrifugation at a high speed (for example, 40,000 rpm) for an hour, all organelles are sedimented and the supernatant fluid contains much of the soluble material of cells, including the protein not bound to membranes. By careful selection of centrifugation speeds, it has been possible to isolate mitochondria, ribosomes, or chloroplasts, shown by visual and biochemical criteria to be reasonably free of contamination by other cell fractions. The central limitation of this method is probably uncertainty about the degree of contamination as well as considerable uncertainty as to the degree of alteration in the properties of organelles due to the

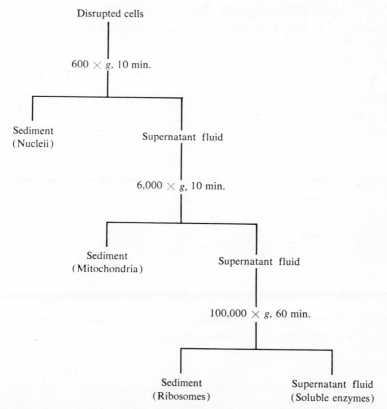

Figure 1–6. *Fractionation of cell components by centrifugation. Disruption of cells, as well as all centrifugations, are carried out under refrigeration. Force required to sediment the various fractions is given as multiples of the force of gravity (g).*

rigors of isolation. For example, conclusions about the properties of mitochondria in intact cells may only be drawn with extreme caution from studies using isolated mitochondria. The most convincing results are those relying on evidence obtained using a variety of techniques.

Suggested Reading

BRACHET, J., *Biochemical Cytology*, Academic Press, New York, 1957.
—— and A. E. MIRKSY (eds.), *The Cell: Biochemistry, Physiology Morphology*, Vol. II, Academic Press, New York, 1961.

DeROBERTIS, E. D. P., W. W. NOWINSKI, and F. A. SAEZ, *Cell Biology*, 4th ed., W. B. Saunders Co., Philadelphia, 1965.

EDSALL, J. T., and J. WYMAN, *Biophysical Chemistry*, Academic Press, New York, 1958.

HENDERSON, L. J., *The Fitness of the Environment*, Macmillan, New York, 1913.

HURRY, S. W., *The Microstructure of Cells*, Houghton Mifflin, Boston, (paper).

RHODIN, J. A. *An Atlas of Ultrastructure*, W. B. Saunders Co., Philadelphia, 1963.

CHAPTER 2

Energy and Control

Cells do things. They move, either internally (the streaming of cytoplasm muscle contraction) or as a unit, through their environment. Cells also carry on a number of less obvious activities, such as the transfer of material through membranes, often against a gradient in concentration, the production of heat, the maintenance of an electrical potential, and the synthesis of an incredible number of chemical compounds. Cells must exert themselves to get ahead in the world or, as we shall see, even to maintain the *status quo*. Exertion means the expenditure of energy, and it seems fair (and necessary) to ask where this energy comes from and how cells apply it to perform such wonders. However, to ask the question on anything but a silly level, it is first necessary to take a serious look at the whole problem of energy, to ask what it is and what forms it can take.

In the life of the cell, the type of energy that is most important is *chemical energy*. It is true that photosynthetic organisms (and therefore the whole living world) obtain energy in the form of radiation, but after the primary absorption event, radiant energy is quickly converted to a chemical form. There are a number of ways in which energy may be transferred, but the cell uses energy of chemical compounds, or, more properly, chemical bonds, as its currency. Therefore, we begin with a consideration of energy as related to chemical reactions

15

and will expand the discussion to other forms of energy as the need arises.

Consider the chemical reaction

$$A \rightleftharpoons B$$

To find out if the reaction is really possible, we begin by throwing in some A and either looking for B to appear or for A to be consumed. There are only two possibilities: A is converted to B or it is not. If it is, we say that the reaction ($A \rightleftharpoons B$) is spontaneous. But, in deciding if a reaction is spontaneous or not, we must include an additional dimension in the reaction scheme, energy.

A spontaneous reaction is an energy-yielding reaction in the sense that it may be used to drive one that is not by itself spontaneous. Energy that is yielded by a spontaneous reaction may be also partly in the form of heat, but this is by no means necessarily the case. Some reactions— including many biological ones—have great capacity to drive other reactions but produce little heat change. Thus we might classify all reactions as energy-yielding and energy-requiring, which is to say spontaneous and not spontaneous. We would write the spontaneous equation involving A and B as

$$A \rightleftharpoons B + \Delta \text{ energy}$$

which is to say that in such a case energy is liberated. A reaction that is not spontaneous in a thermodynamic sense requires energy to make it go. Note that there are two sides to the coin of spontaneity: If a reaction is spontaneous in one direction, it most surely is not in the other. If energy is produced going in one direction, it must be consumed if the reaction is to go in the other.

Note that we do not specify the form in which the energy might exist. In fact, it might consist of mechanical and heat components as well as in other forms. As an example of mechanical energy, one might cite the coupling of chemical reactions to the performance of work, such as gas volume changes against a given pressure or muscular contraction.

At this point it is necessary to observe that there are two senses in which a reaction may or may not proceed. It is possible to write a vast number of reactions that can never work, no matter how much energy be available. These reactions are forbidden for the simple reason that no mechanism exists whereby the transformations may occur. Molecules must obey, not only the laws of thermodynamics, but also such additional restrictions as rules of valence and geometry. The alchemists were notoriously unlucky with such forbidden reactions, finding gold exceedingly hard to produce from base metals, even with the application of considerable energy in the form of heat or good will. Thus the study of energy relationships (thermodynamics) gives information about what is possible but can say nothing about mechanisms or about the rates at which things happen (which may very well be zero).

Free energy

Now, there are a number of ways to express energy, some of which are more applicable to a steam engine than to a reaction within the cell. We shall give the cell first priority and begin by defining a measure of energy which is most suitable to the study of ordinary chemical reactions, the *free energy* of a reaction. Free energy is usually denoted by G (for J. W. Gibbs, one of the founders of modern thermodynamics), and any change in free energy is given as ΔG. So our spontaneous reaction should be written

$$A \rightleftharpoons B + \Delta G$$

For the present, we can define free energy simply as that energy which matters in a chemical reaction, meaning that it determines spontaneity. The ordinary unit of free energy is the calorie, and just as chemical reactions are given in terms of moles, free energy is generally given in terms of calories per mole.

Cell biologists are fortunate in a number of respects (including the interesting nature of the field), and one additional bit of good luck comes to them when they consider energy and energy transformations. The fact is that most cellular reactions take place in solution under more or less constant conditions of temperature, pressure, and volume. Exceptions to this rule would tend to lead to the destruction of cells. This constancy of conditions enables us to ignore a great deal of complication in thermodynamics and make some very pleasant simplifications in our consideration of energy. The treatment that follows will be quite valid for reactions within cells but will be hopelessly inadequate for the study of reactions that might be found inside a volcano or within the cylinder of an automobile.

First, we might dissect the free energy change of a reaction a bit and see how it is put together. We find, for example, that free energy has a sort of double aspect which may be expressed as follows:

Free energy = heat component − order-disorder component

The precise nature of these two components may be stated in the more explicit equation

$$\Delta G = \Delta H - T\Delta S$$

In this equation ΔH represents the change in a quantity called *enthalpy*, which under conditions of constant pressure (which is all that we are interested in) is identical to the change in heat.

It is worth saying a bit more about *heat* (as represented by enthalpy in our discussion). Heat is one of the concepts of thermodynamics that suffers from being too familiar, an everyday idea we are often unable to define because of our certainty about it. For our purposes, heat may be defined as the form of energy that is able to raise the temperature (the molecular kinetic energy) of material. Thus a unit of heat is the calorie, which is the amount of heat required to raise the temperature of 1 gram of water 1 degree centigrade, provided no other energy is exchanged. When one measures the heat absorbed or evolved in a chemical reaction, one detects only the ΔH term of the total free energy. Thus an energy-yielding (spontaneous) reaction might well produce a very low heat of reaction, provided the other term is sufficiently great. It is clearly impossible to predict the free energy of reactions by observations of ΔH alone.

If the enthalpy change is a fairly straightforward change in heat, the order-disorder component requires further discussion. First, in the equation above, T represents the absolute temperature at which the reaction occurs, and ΔS denotes the change in a quantity called *entropy*, which is of great interest to the biologist. Second, since entropy is not measured directly (there is no such thing as an entropy meter), its nature is not as obvious as that of, say, temperature or pressure, which may be sensed directly. Because entropy may have a somewhat unfamiliar ring, we will define it in several ways and trust that the combination of them will be instructive.

DEFINITION 1. *Entropy is a measure of the disorder in a given situation.* For example, a chemical change might well result in a change in the orderliness of the reactants. When one dissolves salt in water, the ions, which were in an extremely orderly state in the precise crystal lattice of the solid, in solution begin flopping about in a quite random manner. In such a case, the event of dissolving would be attended by a large positive change in entropy, ΔS, and in fact any real process, when viewed in a sufficiently broad content, is seen to result in a greater or lesser increase in entropy, which is to say disorder. In this connection, we shall content ourselves (for the moment) with noting that the cell is an extremely orderly configuration of material, so that its formation (or dissolution) should likewise produce a significant ΔS.

DEFINITION 2. *Entropy is a measure of the essential irreversibility of events in the real world.* At this point it is necessary to back down partially on the earlier statement to the effect that reactions tend to be reversible but not fully so. That is, one can never quite get back to the starting point. This may be illustrated by considering a reaction $a \rightleftharpoons b$ and its reverse, $b \rightleftharpoons a$, as a kind of loop:

$$a b$$

From everything we have said, it should be possible to go from a to b with, for example, energy production and then use that energy to go back to a by the other route. There should be no reason why, once started, the reaction could not cycle through a and b endlessly, but in fact this is not observed. At each stage of the cycle, one finds that a little energy becomes unavailable and that, as time runs on, more and more is lost to the system until the whole process grinds to a stop. The fact that energy becomes unavailable in any real process is another way of saying that any real process tends to move in the direction of disorder, and that energy loss in this connection is irrevocable. The energy change in any process related to the loss of order is given by the term $T\,\Delta S$, and the fact that its sign is minus in the definition of ΔG given above is a reflection of its character as a decline in available energy.

DEFINITION 3. Since entropy is central to an understanding of many energy matters, it is vital to be able to measure it. The definition that follows is both the most formal one and that which makes measurement possible. *In a reversible process taking place at constant pressure and absolute temperature T and involving an enthalpy change of dH, the entropy change is given by*

$$S = \int \frac{dH}{T}$$

The essential point is that the entropy contribution to an energy change may be obtained in reversible situations by the relatively simple expedient of measuring a heat change at a known temperature. Thus as real processes approach reversibility, the entropy associated with them becomes increasingly accessible to precise mathematical treatment. In a truly reversible cyclic process (such as the hypothetical one described above), entropy for the entire pathway must be zero, while that associated with any segment of the path is given by the equation above. Clearly, in such a case, there must be regions where a decline in entropy occurs to balance increases found in others.

DEFINITION 4.   A last definition of entropy may be given in terms of probability. We have seen that real reactions are fundamentally irreversible and that disorder (and therefore, entropy) tends to increase in any real process. This is to say that, in the world, disorder is more probable than order and that, by definition, things tend to approach the most probable situation. In the same way, the reason that reactions approach an equilibrium value is that it is the most probable configuration for the reactants and products to assume. A reaction near equilibrium (with its high probability) also becomes increasingly reversible and, for this reason, at equilibrium, entropy production ceases:

$$\frac{dS}{dt} = 0$$

Thus *entropy is closely related to probability*, and it is possible to define it in such terms.

A statistical approach shows that there is a very simple relationship between the probability of a certain state and the entropy change involved in getting there:

$$S = K \ln P$$

where P is the probability of the state, ln is the natural log (to the base e, or $2.718 \ldots$), and K a proportional constant. From this relation it is clear that a very large change in probability, such as that from a structured crystal to a much more random solution, will lead to a large entropy change.

Anyone who has looked at electron micrographs of cells will conclude that the cell is highly improbable (orderly) and that the breakdown of the structure of the cell on death will be associated with a large increase in entropy. Since the dissolution of a cell involves a large energy loss to the $T\Delta S$ term of the free energy expression, it follows that it takes a lot of free energy to make a cell to begin with.

Now, if there is a large energy requirement to achieve this orderly arrangement—the cell—it should also be said that energy is required just to keep a cell orderly and intact. In other words, cells require energy even when they are not growing or making more cells. They require a continuous influx of energy just to keep ahead. The reason for this should be clear from the preceding discussion. Whenever a cell does something, there is a change of free energy, of which a portion is lost forever in the form of the $T\Delta S$ term (entropy). In a sense, order is being constantly siphoned off as cellular events take place, and the maintenance of the supremely orderly and therefore improbable cell requires a continuing uptake of energy throughout its life.

Free energy and equilibria

To see more clearly why free energy (and therefore entropy) is of interest to the biologist, let us return to the general reaction resulting in the transformation of A to B. We have said that the reaction is very nearly reversible and that one might study it going in either direction provided energy is available to drive it in the energetically unfavorable direction. This is a bit too simple, and to see what is going on we must introduce a new aspect of the reaction, its equilibrium. In this connection, it must be said that reactions seldom go all the way. A more likely situation would be for A to become 90 per cent converted to B at the end of the reaction. If this were the case, we would also find that, by starting with B, the reaction would proceed only 10 per cent of the way. In other words, there appears to be an equilibrium position which a reaction will, in time, approach, no matter from which side. The position of the equilibrium is a property of any given reaction and has nothing to do with the rate at which the equilibrium is approached. In our simple case of A $\rightleftharpoons$ B, the equilibrium position may be expressed as the equilibrium constant

$$K = \frac{[B]}{[A]}$$

where [A] and [B] denote the molar concentrations of A and B. If the reaction were more complicated, the equilibrium constant would arise in the same way as the concentrations of the products multiplied together divided by those of the reactants, so that the constant for the conversion of A + B to C + D would be

$$K = \frac{[C][D]}{[A][B]}$$

It is obvious that if the equilibrium of this reaction is far in the direction of the products (C and D), the equilibrium constant will be a large number. It is also clear that when one defines K, it is necessary to specify the direction being considered. The value for K is transformed into its reciprocal by considering the reaction in the opposite direction.

Now, in the light of the equilibrium constant, it is clear that spontaneous reactions are those whose equilibrium lies far in the direction of the products. Under such conditions—when concentrations of reactants are far from their equilibrium values—reactions are able to yield energy rather than require it. This may be expressed by the sign of the free energy change. In the reaction

$$A \rightleftharpoons B$$

if $\Delta G°$, the free energy change with the reactants in the standard state (at a $1M$ concentration at a specified temperature) is positive, the reaction requires added energy to make it go. A negative value, on the other hand, means that the reaction is far from equilibrium and, under those conditions, spontaneous and energy-yielding.

If the sign of $\Delta G°$ tells whether the reaction is spontaneous or not, the magnitude of $\Delta G°$ should tell us something about the actual position of the equilibrium. This is the case, and a simple equation gives the relationship between the two as

$$-\Delta G° = RT \ln K$$

where $\Delta G°$ is again the change in free energy under standard conditions, R is the gas constant,* T the absolute temperature, and K the equilibrium constant of the reaction. Since R and T are both positive, it is clear that when $\Delta G°$ is positive $\ln K$ must be negative and therefore K must be between 0 and 1. When $\Delta G°$ is 0, since neither R nor T can be 0, $\ln K$ must be 0 and therefore K must equal 1. Finally, when $\Delta G°$ is negative, the same argument leads to the conclusion that K must be greater than 1. (see Figure 2–1).

* $R = 1.98$ calories per mole-degree.

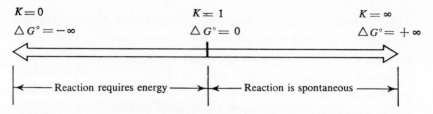

Figure 2–1. *The relationship between equilibrium constant (K) and standard free energy change ($\Delta G°$).*

The close relationship between equilibrium and free energy change is of great importance to the biologist, because energy is required for the support of life. This means that many of the reactions of life are unfavorably situated with regard to their equilibria. To proceed, they must somehow be coupled to reactions that are, themselves, spontaneous. This sort of coupling may be given, in the simplest case, as one reaction pulling another by removing products. If the reaction

$$A \rightleftharpoons B$$

is not spontaneous (if its equilibrium is far to the left), any spontaneous reaction resulting in the removal of B will tend to pull the first. For example,

$$B \rightleftharpoons C$$

may proceed well and be far removed from equilibrium. If this is so, the net reaction

$$A \rightleftharpoons B \rightleftharpoons C$$

will go nicely. It should be intuitively clear that the progress of the whole coupled reaction to the right will depend on whether the equilibrium of $B \rightleftharpoons C$ is farther to the right than that of $A \rightleftharpoons B$ is to the left; the reaction farthest removed from its equilibrium will win out.

It should be clear that the same result can be given in terms of the $\Delta G°$'s. We can express it by saying that a reaction with a negative free energy change may drive a reaction with a positive one. This may be put differently by writing the net reaction as the sum of the two parts:

$$
\begin{aligned}
A &\rightleftharpoons B \qquad \Delta G_1° \\
B &\rightleftharpoons C \qquad \Delta G_2° \\
\hline
A &\rightleftharpoons C \qquad \Delta G_1° + \Delta G_2°
\end{aligned}
$$

Thus, if there is to be a net reaction $A \to C$, $\Delta G_1^\circ + \Delta G_2^\circ$ must be less than zero. A biologist might put this still differently and say that energy-producing reactions drive energy-requiring reactions. In fact, in the biological world, discounting recourse to magic, the only way in which one reaction may drive another, and hence the only way that free energy may be transferred between one set of reactants and another, is by a sequence of reactions such as

$$A \rightleftharpoons B \rightleftharpoons C$$

where one reaction pulls another by virtue of the relative positions of their equilibria. It is clear that much of the complex array of metabolic reactions is nothing more than a mechanism for the linkage of unfavorable (and energy-requiring) reactions, such as the syntheses of cell constituents, with those that are farther from their equilibria (energy-producing), such as the metabolic breakdown of sugars.

An electrochemical version of free energy

The reader is aware from a course in introductory chemistry that many reactions involving the movement of electrons (oxidation or reduction) may be followed electrically by the movement of those electrons. Such a situation is called an *electrochemical cell* and, without considering the experimental details, it is worth noting that there is a direct relationship between the electrical work done by such a reaction and its free energy change. In other words, the electrical work is done totally at the expense of free energy, and the relation between the two is given as

$$\Delta G^\circ = -n^\circ \mathscr{F} \Delta E^\circ$$

where ΔG° is the standard free energy change, ΔE° the standard potential (in volts), n the number of electrons transferred per molecule of reactant, and $\mathscr{F}$, the Faraday, is a constant representing the electrical capacity to do work and equals 96,500 coulombs. Since free energy changes are generally given in terms of calories, a more useful figure for $\mathscr{F}$ is 23,063 calories per volt.

The electrochemical representation of free energy is of interest to biologists mostly in the study of such oxidation-reductions as the electron-transferring reactions of the cytochrome chain (see Chapter 6). In many such cases, measurements of equilibrium constant are well-nigh impossible, but electrical measurements are quite accessible and hence provide a means of obtaining thermodynamic information. Inasmuch as these electron-transferring reactions are central to cellular energy production, knowledge about free energy changes is especially desirable.

The influence of pH on free energy changes

The importance of specifying conditions under which free energy changes are measured has been mentioned. The standard free energy changes given thus far have referred to standard conditions, where reactants are at $1M$ concentrations. This means that, when H^+ is involved in a reaction, standard state implies an H^+ concentration of $1\ M$, which is pH 0 (see the definition of pH below). This is hardly a physiological pH, and, in treatments related to biological chemistry, standard conditions are often redefined as at pH 7. It is obviously important to be clear as to what pH is specified in a given discussion. It is also clearly useful to have in hand an expression relating a change in $\Delta G°$ to a change in pH. Such an equation is easy to derive* and, for the case where hydrogen ion is a product of the reaction, may be written

$$\Delta G°' = \Delta G° - 2.303RT(\text{pH})$$

where $\Delta G°'$ is the standard free energy change at the given pH, $\Delta G°$ that at pH 0, R the gas constant, and T the absolute temperature. "pH" refers to the pH at which the reaction is actually measured. This equation serves as evidence that the conditions under which a free energy change takes place are able to affect the magnitude of the change and must always be specified in any real situation.

The steady state

Most of the preceding discussion of energy is strictly applicable only to completely reversible processes, which is to say those which are at equilibrium. Thus calculations of free energy related to biological reactions, are valid only when the reactions are at equilibrium. Such situations seldom (or never) obtain in living cells. In general, cellular

* The interested reader may follow the derivation by considering the relation between $\Delta G°$ and K and including the hydrogen ion concentration in the equilibrium. This strategy, together with the definition of pH as $-1/\log[H^+]$, should suffice.

reactions tend to be very far removed from their equilibria, so that thermodynamic calculations represent limiting cases from which it is often quite impossible to derive useful information. In other words, the essentially "closed" systems studied at equilibrium do not give results directly applicable to the cell, which is often described as "open," with a significant flow of nutrient, waste product, and heat across its boundaries. Furthermore, ordinary thermodynamic arguments involve scalar quantities, which fail to reflect the vectoral character of many cellular events. For example, many chemical transformations of the cell involve the transport of molecules across a membrane or are directed with respect to an enzyme surface, and it is important that the vectoral aspects of such matters be included in energetic considerations.

Although the area of nonequilibrium thermodynamics involves somewhat formidable mathematics and is largely outside the scope of this book, it is worth considering one central feature of it, the idea of the steady state, which replaces the central role of the equilibrium in ordinary thermodynamics.

If one considers systems that do not come to equilibrium, it is useful to think in terms of flow, whether it be flow of molecules through a membrane, flow of heat between regions of different temperature, or the flow of matter through a biochemical pathway. Furthermore, in extending the analogy with liquid flow, one might say that a flow is proportional to some sort of driving force. This might be written, in the simplest case,

$$J = XL$$

where J is a vector representing a flow rate, L a vector representing the driving force, and X a proportionality constant (scalar). The driving force might be a pressure (driving a liquid flow), the difference between concentrations of some compound on two sides of a membrane (driving transport across the membrane), or the free energy difference in a series of reactions.

The mathematical description of flow can in many instances be horribly complex, but there is one situation, the *steady state*, that represents both relative simplicity and applicability to the processes of life. A process is in the steady state when its properties are not changing in time. An example of the steady state is found in a river that is flowing at a uniform rate, so that, for each arbitrary segment, as much water enters as leaves (see Figure 2–2). Examples of the steady state on the

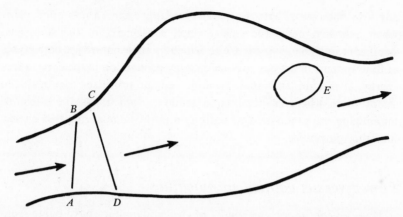

Figure 2–2. *Illustration of the steady state. In any arbitrary portion of the river, exactly as much water enters as leaves, so that the amount of water in that portion remains constant. This applies to the space within lines ABCD as well as to that within line E.*

cellular scale include a portion of a metabolic pathway where an intermediate is formed and utilized at the same rate, so that its concentration remains constant with time. Other examples will be discussed in later chapters.

Clearly, in connection with a system at the steady state, thermodynamic functions such as energy and entropy take on a different aspect. For example, differences in free energy or electrochemical potential may be regarded as elements of the driving force instead of parameters of a stationary equilibrium situation. Similarly, we found that entropy does not change in a system at equilibrium, although it is continuously produced in flowing systems. Indeed, it is possible to define equilibrium as that condition where

$$\frac{dS}{dt} = 0$$

and the steady state as that where

$$\frac{dS}{dt} = \text{a constant}$$

The constant production of entropy in steady-state systems is a central feature of such systems, with important consequences for the cell. In addition, the rate of entropy production approaches a minimum value when a system nears the steady state, a property of the state also significant in its description. Cells, which by their nature are collections of flow systems, must pay for any entropy production in the coin of free energy. It is significant that dynamic cellular processes approach the steady state wherever possible, a tendency which has the effect of minimizing the production of entropy and thus conserving free energy for other purposes.

Power versus control in machines

Many of the important results of thermodynamics have come from the study of energy transformations involved in the action of man-made machines, such as steam or hot-air engines. This portion of classical thermodynamics remains somewhat inaccessible to the biologist, owing to superficial dissimilarities between energy as applied to an engine and as involved in a reaction within the cell. Nonetheless, the study of machines has provided interesting analogies for those involved in the living world, and the recent development of information theory and the study of servomechanisms suggests that the end of such analogies is not in sight.

For our purposes, a machine is something that does work, and doing work means quite literally using energy. In other words, a machine might lift something and take in energy to do so. It should be obvious that the ability of the machine to work is limited by the design of the machine and related matters such as efficiency but, most fundamentally, by the energy at hand. A machine cannot expend in work any more energy than it has available, a truth known, in various guises, as the *first law of thermodynamics*. It may also be expressed by saying that energy may be neither created nor destroyed, or by asserting that "you can't get something for nothing."* In any case, the relation between power input and work output by machines is well known and valuable to us in our general understanding of energy (see Figure 2–3).

However, contemporary machines are noted for doing more than converting energy into brute work. Most of the advances in machine design during the present century have been related, not to the problem

---

* The *second law of thermodynamics*, which is based on the nonreversibility of real processes, adds that "you can't even break even."

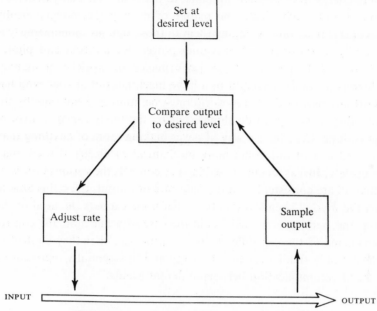

Figure 2–3.   *Outline of feedback control.*

of how to get more work out of a mechanical system, but, more, how to control that work to a higher degree. Machines have evolved to the extent where the control is impressive indeed, culminating (for the present) in automated machines of fantastic subtlety.

These advances suggest that the design of machines, from an energy point of view, involves two separate but related systems, the power part and the control part. Both require energy, and both must be taken into consideration when the energy input and output of a machine is considered, but it appears universal that the power system uses the lion's share of the total energy available. The dramatic automation of a mechanical process is added to the uncontrolled process at a surprisingly low expense of additional energy. Control of the utilization of incredible amounts of energy is effected by machinery using almost no energy at all but operating with great delicacy and precision. An example might be the home furnace, which transmits the chemical energy of fuel into heat on a large scale but is under the control of a thermostat, whose power requirements are indeed minimal.

The distinction between power and control is equally valid in consideration of energy transformations by the cell. We have said that cells require energy in respectable amounts to perform their many activities, chemical and mechanical. The matter of driving thermodynamically unfavorable reactions by linking them to those that go spontaneously is essentially in the realm of providing power. Respiration and photosynthesis supply power for the performance of work in a manner analogous to the power input of a large machine. But anyone who has studied any part of the living world must be impressed not only by the availability of energy to do things, but by the finely tuned control of what is done. Cells have a way of never making more of anything than they need and of not doing more mechanical or electrical work than appropriate. Just as an automated factory controls the various processes so that all are consistent with the final rate of output, the cell is able to mesh the myriad chemical events so that none exceeds the need of the whole and nothing is wasted. As in the case of a machine, the control mechanisms of the cell differ from the processes that they control in requiring only small amounts of energy and in essentially representing modes of communication between different events.

Control through feedback

In discussing the exact form that control mechanisms in machines or cells may take, it is useful to return to the example of the home furnace and its control by a thermostat. The operation of such a device is familiar to everyone from a temperate climate, and the thermostat may be taken as a basic specimen of a feedback mechanism. To begin with, the role of a furnace is to provide heat: a question of power. But a furnace that does nothing but provide heat is thought by many to be a rather barbaric form of machine. A more acceptable one would be a furnace that could provide just the right amount of heat, that would maintain a set and civilized temperature within a house. Excluding difficulties in deciding what represents a civilized temperature, it must be said that the task of the furnace is then a difficult one and must suddenly add several functions to the one of transferring heat.

In the first place, the system must be able to measure the temperature to see how it is doing. There must be a provision for comparing the actual temperature with the temperature at which the thermostat is set. The system must convert any difference between the two into a signal which will communicate to the power end of things (the furnace) the need for more or less heat. To make matters more difficult, furnaces generally exist in two states, on and off, and humans (especially Americans, it is claimed) tend to be rather particular about the temperature not fluctuating wildly. Clearly, the message from the thermostat must be of a yes-or-no character, but it must be at the same time capable of avoiding excessively uneven output. Thus the control mechanism must have the ability to sense the difference between the desired output and the actual situation, and to encode the difference in a form which is understandable to the machine producing the output. The requirements for control on the cellular scale will be seen to be the same.

For example, a basic and typical control problem on the cellular scale is that of making enough, but not too much, of some cell product. An amino acid should be synthesized at a rate sufficient to allow its use in the manufacture of protein, but there is little benefit—and possibly considerable harm—in making an excess. The synthetic machinery of the cell faces a problem identical to that of the thermostat in most details. The amount of product of a set of reactions must be somehow monitored and compared to the required amount. If there is found to be an excess, somehow the synthetic route must be shut off until the proper level is attained. Such a situation, where excess output leads to a shutting off, is called *negative feedback* and is extremely common in the biological world. In the case of amino acid synthesis, feedback control is exerted either by the inhibition by the final product of an enzyme involved in the synthesis (see Chapter 3) or by the suppression of the synthesis of an enzyme, again by the final product (see Chapter 4). Thus, in both mechanisms, the formation of an excess of the amino acid (or whatever) leads to a reduction in its rate of synthesis, thereby maintaining a suitable level. The reverse sort of feedback, not surprisingly termed *positive feedback*, is less prevalent (or less obvious) but examples do exist in the economy of the cell, perhaps most clearly in the case of glycolysis, where ATP stimulates a process leading to its synthesis (see Chapter 5).

Information transfer

It should be clear that feedback control of some event, whether it be in a machine or a cell, involves the problem of communication between the input and output. The information about output must be compared (an algebraic operation) with a set value and then communicated to another part of the whole process, whereby the rate is regulated. This sort of information transfer is, perhaps, the least complicated of the many encountered in the cell. In fact, any form of regulation in cellular processes must involve some form of information transfer. As the fundamental basis for the regulation of the activities of living things resides in the genetic systems of the organism, it is not at all odd that the terminology of modern genetics is full of references to information storage and transfer. Such phrases as the "genetic code," "genetic information," and "nonsense" suggest a debt to information theory that is not accidental.

To be more explicit about the role of information in cellular affairs, we should first be a bit more exact about what we mean by information. The difficulty in talking about information is that everyone has a general sort of idea about what it is and therefore it resists exact description. Let us then be formal and unbending and look at information in fairly

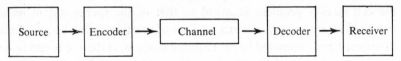

Figure 2–4.   *An information transfer system.*

explicit terms. Figure 2–4 shows a generalized system for information transfer, whether in the cell or at both ends of a telegraph line. Information is encoded at the source and decoded at the receiver. The idea of information as a code means only that if one sends information about a thing (such as the heat content of a living room in our example above), one does not need to send the thing itself. If one wishes to send the information that it is raining in Moose Jaw, it is not required to send a bucket of rainwater; it would be adequate (and even preferable) to send a message, and in this case the code would probably be something approximating the English language.

In our diagram, the information is said to be carried on a channel, which is nothing more than the physical mechanism for communication. An information channel might be a telegraph wire, an electromagnetic vibration of such-and-such a frequency, or a series of linked reactions in the chemistry of the cell. The channel is distinguished by having a limit on its ability to carry information and by the fact that it is susceptible to random interference, called *noise*, of which radio static is an example. Noise tends to limit information transfer and can be countered by such devices as repeating portions of the message (redundancy), which, however, obviously decreases efficiency.

Noise is a very useful concept in this connection and has been applied to the cell in the context of genetic mutations as random interference in genetic information transfer. Indeed, a consideration of what noise is, and specifically why it is not information, can give insight into the character of information itself. Consider (in Figure 2–5) an information source emitting a signal. The reader is asked to decide whether this is, in any sense, information, but without knowing anything about what goes on inside the source. The signal might be information or, conversely, it might be nonsense (a signal lacking information), perhaps due to an infinitely noisy channel. How can one decide? One might be tempted to note that real information should be orderly and the remark "emgfithe-eikkkmrughf," while perhaps eloquent if delivered with feeling, could

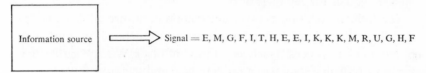

Information source ⟹ Signal = E, M, G, F, I, T, H, E, E, I, K, K, K, M, R, U, G, H, F

Figure 2–5. *An information source generating a signal.*

hardly be called orderly. But that is the problem: Order, like beauty, is at least partly in the eye of the beholder. The signal emitted by our source might well be completely random (without order), made up from random spins of a roulette wheel. But it is also possible that it could be meaningful and even beautiful to a Basque shepherd. Finally, it might be a pre-arranged signal meaning something like "help," or "it is raining in Moose Jaw," or perhaps both. Just looking at the signal, we are hard pressed to decide if there is any information at all, and this inability leads to a fundamental conclusion about information transfer. It is clear that any decisions about information require the presence of a source *and* a receiver able to receive, that is, decode. Information without a receiver just does not exist.

But there is yet another restriction on what information is. Not only must a recipient exist, but the communication must say something to it that is really information in the sense that it did not "know" it already. This very important restriction means that even if the code is recognizable, the message must say something not totally irrelevant. If I am in Moose Jaw, and I receive the glad tidings that "it is raining in Moose Jaw" while the rain drips down my nose, the information content of that message is rather low, in both a colloquial and strict sense. Since I was completely certain about it to begin with, I gained nothing from the message. Had I been only about 50 per cent sure to begin with, the message would have increased the probability for me from 0.5 to 1, and the increase in probability would give a measure of the information transferred. This is true of all information transfer, and one can thus define information in terms of its ability to increase the probability of something being true. This may be stated

$$\text{Information} = -\log P$$

where P is the probability of the message being known to begin with and the log taken to any base that is convenient. Note that if a message is totally certain to begin with, $P = 1$, and the information content of the message equals the log of 1, or 0.

The intimate relation between information and probability may be seen in another light by examining a message generated by some completely random process (such as a throw of dice). We saw earlier that the most probable state was a random one, and therefore a completely random message is completely probable—$P = 1$. If the message is totally probable, it is totally predictable and therefore completely unable to decrease our uncertainty about anything. Therefore, the information content is zero.

Entropy and information

We said earlier in the chapter that real events tended to slip in the direction of disorder, which was more probable than order. This slippage was represented as entropy in some of our equations, and entropy was thus defined as a measure of probability. We have now discovered that *information* is related to probability in a similar fashion. Obviously there is some connection between the two, and it is interesting that information theorists have a habit of using the terms information and entropy interchangeably.

Since a change in entropy is also a change in energy, it follows that information is also a species of energy. Whenever information is transferred, energy is consumed. One does not obtain order out of disorder without putting in energy. Writers about biological matters are fond of pointing out that the orderly character of a cell represents an island in a sea of disorder and that cells (and organisms) must obtain energy to combat the increase in disorder (entropy) that accompanies any process.

Some have spoken of organisms feeding on negative entropy (which one might wish to call information) in order to obtain order. Although this does not perhaps help very much in the sense of suggesting concrete experimental approaches to the living world, it is certainly true that the maintenance of order through the specific control mechanisms of the cell does require some energy. It is likewise clear that energy "used up" in information and control is very like entropy, and that the only source of it in the cellular world is in the free energy changes accompanying spontaneous reactions.

Suggested Reading

FRUTON, J. S., and S. SIMMONDS, *General Biochemistry*, John Wiley & Sons, New York, 2nd ed., 1960, Chap. 9.

GEORGE, F. H., *Cybernetics and Biology*, W. H. Freeman & Co., San Francisco, 1965.

KATCHALSKY, A., and P. F. CURRAN, *Nonequilibrium Thermodynamics in Biophysics*, Harvard University Press, Cambridge, 1965.

KLOTZ, I., *Introduction to Chemical Thermodynamics*, W. A. Benjamin, New York, 1964.

WIENER, N., *Cybernetics*, MIT Press, Cambridge, 2nd ed., 1961.

CHAPTER 3

Proteins and Enzymes

The class of compounds called *proteins* comprises about 15 per cent of the total mass of cells. They represent important structural elements of the cell, membranes being about one-half protein, and it is obvious that changes in the cell environment affecting the properties of protein will produce important effects. Moreover, nearly all proteins exhibit enzymic activity—are able to serve as catalysts in one or more biochemical reactions—and again, it is clear that small changes in environment which influence proteins will produce dramatic alterations in the metabolic processes of the cell.

Amino acids

Proteins are polymers composed of *amino acids*, and many of the properties of the whole protein reflect those of the subunit. Proteins differ from such polymers as glycogen, which are made up of many identical units, in incorporating various amino acids in a single molecule, thus permitting enormous variety. Most amino acids may be described by the general formula

$$\begin{array}{c} \text{R} \\ | \\ \text{H}_2\text{N}-\text{C}-\text{COOH} \\ | \\ \text{H} \end{array}$$

where R represents a chemical group which might be H (glycine), CH_3 (alanine), $-CH_2SH$ (cysteine), or any one of 16 or so others. Ignoring the nature of the possible R groups (which are summarized in Figure 3–1), the amino acid is seen to have two functional groups, a basic amino group and an acidic carboxyl group. These account for two most important properties of amino acids, their interaction with hydrogen ion and their coupling together to form protein. In the first case, it is important to note that these compounds have, discounting the R group, two sites where ionization can take place and therefore where hydrogen ion concentration can have an effect. Above pH 2, the carboxyl group becomes ionized,

$$COOH \rightleftharpoons COO^- + H^+$$

whereas below pH 8 to 9, the amino group becomes positively charged,

$$NH_2 + H^+ \rightleftharpoons NH_3^+$$

Thus the exact state of the amino acid depends sharply on the pH at which it finds itself, and properties change accordingly. At neutral pH, two major contributions to the structure will be the double (dipolar) ion,

$$^+H_3N-\overset{\displaystyle R}{\underset{\displaystyle H}{\overset{|}{\underset{|}{C}}}}-COO^-$$

In no case does the uncharged species (the way one normally writes the structure) predominate in aqueous solution. In fact, with many amino acids (see Figure 3–1) additional reactions with H^+ are possible, because of the presence of ionizable R groups, and the sum of possible interactions may become quite complex. However, since most biological functions of amino acids occur in the vicinity of neutral pH, the more complicated interactions may be ignored.

All of this is to say that the hydrogen ion concentration in the environment of an amino acid or protein may influence its state in a significant way. On the other hand, amino acids, either alone or linked in a protein, influence the environment in the sense that they can serve as a buffer. The functional groups maintain a stable pH by taking up or expelling H^+ as the H^+ concentration fluctuates, thereby counteracting these fluctuations. The action of amino acids as both weak acids and

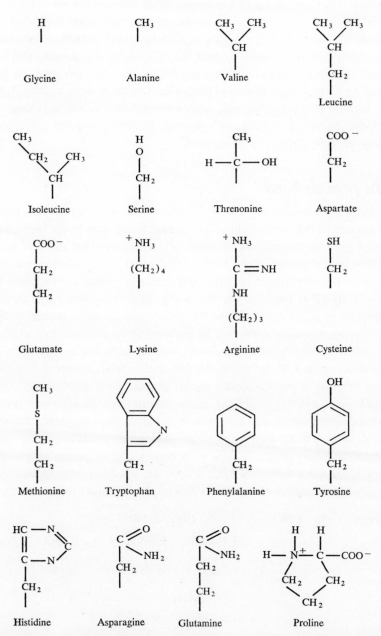

Figure 3–1. *Functional groups of important amino acids. Since proline is not a typical alpha amino acid, its entire structure is shown.*

bases spreads the stabilizing influence over a considerable range of pH, and it is precisely this wide range that makes amino acids effective buffers. The side chains of the amino acids provide the proteins with large numbers of free ionizable groups, giving them impressive buffering capability. Since the free amino acid content in the cell tends to be quite low relative to the content in proteins, it is likely that protein plays a major role in keeping the interior of cells at the stable pH required for stability of function. The role of amino acids as pH stabilizers extends to a practical level, as they are often included in reaction mixtures in enzyme studies as buffers, with glycine, histidine, and the dipeptide, glycyl-glycine, frequently being used.

The peptide bond

Although amino acids possess properties and undergo many reactions of interest to the organic chemist, it is safe to say that in the biological world one reaction eclipses all others in importance. That reaction is, of course, the formation of the *peptide bond*, which enables amino acids to serve as the subunits of peptides and proteins, giving them a place in practically all activities of the cell. Since the only two chemical groups common to all amino acids are the amino and carboxyl groups, polymerization of amino acids may be expected to involve these structures. In fact, amino acids polymerize to form proteins by the condensation of the amino group of one molecule with the carboxyl group of another, thus forming a peptide bond. As an example, we may consider the synthesis of a dimer of glycine, glycyl glycine, but the argument holds for the formation of any polypeptide. Note, in the first place, that the condensation of an amino and a carboxyl group is nothing more than formation of an amide linkage with elimination of water, a fact not altered by the presence of both groups on one molecular species. An amide condensation of two molecules of glycine might then be written

$$^+H_3N—CH_2—COO^- + {}^+H_3N—CH_2—COO^- \rightleftharpoons$$
$$^+H_3N—CH_2—CONH—CH_2—COO^- + H_2O$$

and the peptide (amide) linkage could be written more explicitly as

$$\begin{matrix} O & H \\ \| & | \\ —C— & N— \end{matrix}$$

In addition, the reverse reaction is possible, and the peptide bond may be hydrolyzed (the water put back) either in an enzyme-catalyzed reaction or under extreme conditions of pH, either acidic or basic. This reversal of peptide bond synthesis is essentially what takes place with the action of proteolytic (protein hydrolyzing) enzymes involved in digestion, and the products are free amino acids.

Levels of protein structure

Since it is clear that what works in the synthesis of a dipeptide also works in the synthesis of a protein, although on a larger scale, one might suppose that protein structure (and therefore enzyme structure) would be simply a question of amino acid content. This would be the case if proteins were simple polymers of one amino acid, but the actual situation is more complex. Nearly all proteins, whether they have several hundred subunits or only 50, contain from 15 to 20 different kinds of amino acid. Thus knowledge of the structure must include, as a minimum, not only information about amino acid content, but also their sequence in the protein chain. Although many proteins have been purified and examined carefully for amino acid composition, knowledge about sequence is slow and difficult, and the amino acid sequence of only a few proteins has been obtained to date.

In those few cases where the unique sequence of amino acids in a protein (primary structure) is known, one might regard the structure as fully elucidated, but, in fact, even the heroic efforts of protein chemists in this area have failed to give us the complete picture. Although our knowledge of the sequence of subunits may be complete, the most interesting aspect of structure (especially with regard to enzyme action) has to do with the three-dimensional configuration of the protein in space—the way that the chain might be coiled or wrapped around itself.

Studies of a number of proteins by X-ray diffraction have led to the conclusion that there is a repeating three-dimensional unit found in a large number of different proteins. A considerable portion of the total chain length of many proteins appears to consist of a helical configuration, with an average of 3.6 amino acids per turn of the helix. This arrangement of the protein chain in space is called the *secondary* structure and is consistent with what is known about the bond angles and hydrogen-bonding capability of amino acids. Now, if one imagines a protein to be composed of a chain (primary structure) where large portions of the chain are in the form of a regular coil, then the actual dis-position of that coil in space represents the *tertiary structure*. The chain, helical regions and all, is seen to be wrapped about itself in an exceedingly complex but consistent fashion, often forming a rather compact, globular molecule. Owing to advances in the technique of X-ray dif-fraction and the development of electronic computational methods for analyzing data, considerably more extensive and detailed information is available about the tertiary structure of proteins than about the primary structure which is not at all alarming in view of the fact that it is the tertiary structure that appears to be most relevant in the analysis of enzyme action.

One might well wonder what the mechanism could be for winding and coiling in so complex and specific a manner. In fact, it appears that there need be no special mechanism at all, for the secondary and tertiary structures follow inevitably from the amino acid sequence. In other words, the final total structure is the most favored one in a thermo-dynamic sense and, given the proper sequence, the protein approaches the correct configuration spontaneously. The structure is determined by intramolecular electrostatic and hydrogen bonds as well as by a limited number of covalent interactions between the individual amino acids of the chain. The spontaneity of tertiary structure may be seen in the instance where it may be disarranged by heat treatment and then recon-stituted, a process usually called *reversible denaturation*.

Enzymes as proteins

All enzymes are certainly proteins, and many of their properties reflect those of proteins in general. For example, enzymes are sensitive to extremes of heat and hydrogen ion concentration, so the isolation of enzymes from tissue must be carried out at carefully controlled pH and usually at a low temperature. Furthermore, the action of enzymes often exhibits a sharp temperature and pH optimum, the reasons for which may be attributed to the properties of proteins and even amino acids.

Figure 3–2 shows the influence of pH on an enzyme-catalyzed reaction and indicates that the measurement of enzyme reactions must always take it into consideration. The exact position of the pH optimum differs for different enzymes, but is often in the region of neutrality. From Figure 3–3 one can see that an enzyme exhibits an optimum for tem-perature as well.

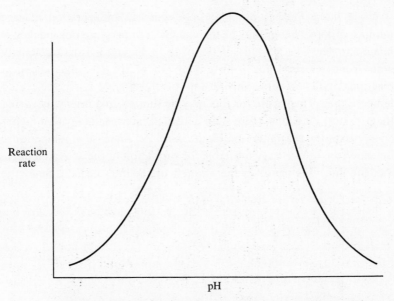

Figure 3–2.   *Influence of pH on enzyme activity.*

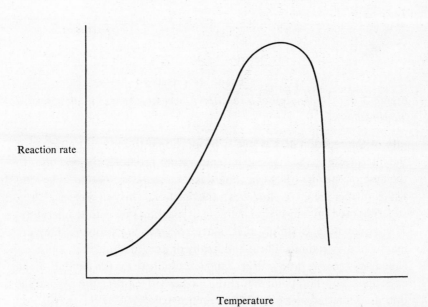

Figure 3–3.   *Influence of temperature on enzyme activity.*

While the pH effect probably represents an influence on a large number of ionizable groups of the enzyme, temperature dependency is much simpler. The left side of the peak in Figure 3–3 (rising activity with rising temperature) is an expression of the fact that chemical reactions of all sorts are temperature-sensitive and go faster at elevated temperatures. The reason for this may be summarized briefly by saying that, in most reactions, there is an activated intermediate with a higher energy than the reactants (see Figure 3–4). An increase in temperature increases the total energy available for formation of the activated intermediate and thus increases the amount of the intermediate. Since the

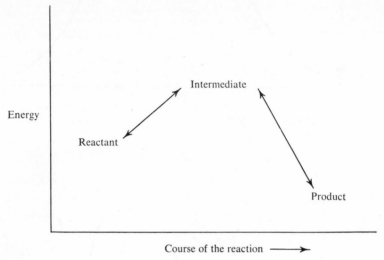

Figure 3–4. *Mechanism of a reaction proceeding by way of an activated intermediate.*

rate of the reaction as a whole is proportional to the concentration of the intermediate, the increase in temperature promotes the reaction. In the case of enzymes, however, there is a temperature optimum beyond which further increases slow down the reaction. This is a separate effect, superimposed on the general increase of reaction rate with temperature. The explanation is simply that, since enzymes are proteins, they are inactivated by too much heat and finally destroyed altogether, a process called *irreversible denaturation* (and exemplified by the boiling of an egg). The important point is that the increase in temperature beyond the optimum interferes—not with the reaction catalyzed by the enzyme but with the integrity of the enzyme itself.

The rate of enzyme reactions

To say anything intelligible about the role and regulation of enzymes within the intact cell, it is first necessary to examine the exact mechanism of enzyme catalysis in a little detail. We may begin by noting that the role of enzymes is simply to promote reactions (make them go faster). For example, consider the reaction

$$A \rightleftharpoons B$$

Let us imagine that this reaction is thermodynamically possible. Now, even though the reaction may be spontaneous, it may be slow. It might require several years to be detactable. The cell cannot usually afford to wait, and it is not surprising that the addition of the specific enzyme that converts A to B might well accelerate the rate several millionfold.

Another property of the reaction $A \rightleftharpoons B$ is the position of equilibrium (see Chapter 2). The position of equilibrium is given by the equilibrium constant

$$K = \frac{[B]}{[A]}$$

and is a thermodynamic property of the reaction. Now, a very important feature of enzymes is that, although they greatly accelerate the reaction, they do not shift the equilibrium. K is K no matter what; with an enzyme, you just get there quicker. A more general way of saying the same thing is that enzymes do not alter thermodynamic properties of reactions, only the kinetic ones (those having to do with rates).

The specificity of enzymes

From the point of view of the biologist, one of the most important aspects of enzyme action is its high degree of specificity. An enzyme which reacts with, say, glucose will not be likely to react at a comparable rate with any other sugar, however similar to glucose in structure. Although some enzymes are less particular about their substrate than this, reacting for example with all D-amino acids, they are exceptions. This specificity of enzymes, taken together with the very large number of chemical reactions occurring in a cell, suggests that each cell must contain an extensive selection of enzymes in order to manage the totality of metabolism.

Furthermore, the fact that single enzymes do not promote a number of different reactions enables one to speak of metabolic pathways where a sequence of enzymes directs a flow of compounds along a well-defined route. It is very important to point out that enzyme specificity leads directly to the possibility of tightly controlled metabolism, since it is quite possible for a single enzyme to be crucial in the synthesis of a given end product. Since this enzyme is generally doing nothing else, it is possible to turn the pathway on or off by controlling the synthesis or reactivity of the individual enzyme, which becomes a control point for the pathway.

The control of enzymic reaction rates by reactant concentration

The small molecule which reacts in the presence of enzyme is called the *substrate*, an unfortunate term, but one in general use. It is possible to alter the rate of an enzymic reaction by changing the concentration of the substrate, a reflection of the more general fact that chemical reactions tend to depend on concentration. In the simplest case of a nonenzymic reaction, the velocity of conversion of A to B may be described as

$$\frac{dA}{dt} = k[\text{A}] \qquad \text{(Eq. 1)}$$

where dA/dt is the velocity of the reaction, [A] the concentration of A, and k the rate constant of the reaction. In this simple case where velocity is dependent on the concentration of a single reactant, the reaction is called a *first-order reaction*, and k is known as the first-order rate constant. Were there two reactants, such as in the reaction

$$\text{A} + \text{B} \rightleftharpoons \text{C}$$

the expression for velocity would become

$$\frac{dA}{dt} = k[\text{A}][\text{B}] \qquad \text{(Eq. 2)}$$

Now the expression for the rate of an enzymic reaction will be more complicated than this simple case. However, it remains true, as in these equations, that the rate of an enzymic reaction is proportional to con-

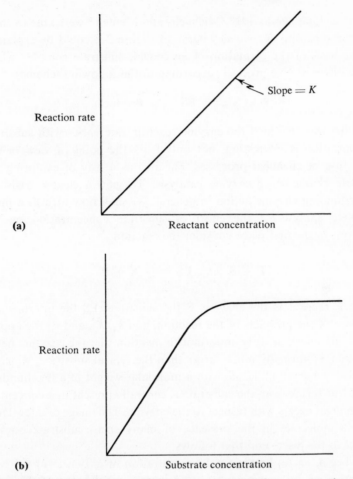

Figure 3-5. *The influence of reactant concentration on reaction rate.* (a) *A first order reaction.* (b) *An enzymic reaction.*

centrations of reactants. This is seen in Figure 3–5, which shows the effect of plotting velocity against concentration in the case of both first-order reactions and those mediated by enzymes. In the case of the first-order reaction, one finds a straight line of which the slope is the rate constant *k*. In the enzymic reaction, things are less clear: There appears to be a region where rate is proportional to substrate concentration, but this passes into a region of the curve where additional substrate makes little difference in the reaction rate.

This curve represents results from a large number of experiments performed with a large number of enzymes over the last half-century.

Indeed as long ago as 1913, Michaelis and Menten* were able to show that the substrate dependency curve of Figure 3–5 could be explained on the basis of the formation of an enzyme-substrate complex which broke down to give products according to the following scheme:

$$E + S \rightleftharpoons ES \longrightarrow Products$$

Thus the way in which the enzyme reaction rate varies with substrate concentration is interesting, not only from the point of view of cell regulation of chemical processes, but also as a way of exploring the intimate character of enzyme catalysis. To gain a clearer basis for understanding enzyme action in general, we shall now turn to a more complete analysis of the effect of substrate concentration on the reaction. In the first place consider the reaction

$$E + S \underset{k_2}{\overset{k_1}{\rightleftharpoons}} ES \overset{k_3}{\longrightarrow} X + E$$

where E represents the enzyme, S the substrate, ES the intermediate complex, X the products of the reaction, and k_1, k_2, and k_3 the appropriate rate constant. It is important to mention that the enzyme, being a protein, is normally much larger than the typical substrate, which is commonly a small molecule with a molecular weight of a few hundred or so. For this reason, the substrate is generally present in a concentration in great excess with respect to the enzyme. The image of a few large enzyme molecules in the presence of many small substrate ones is central to the discussion that follows.

To begin, let [e] be the total concentration of enzyme, [p] the concentration of the enzyme-substrate complex, and [s] that of the substrate. At any given moment during the reaction, some of the enzyme will actually be part of the complex, so that the concentration of *free* enzyme is given by [e − p]. Since the substrate is present in huge excess when compared to the enzyme-substrate complex, we can ignore the vanishingly small amount of substrate taking part in the complex. In other words, [s] and [s − p] are, for all practical purposes, equal.

Finally, one other assumption is necessary before beginning. Since there are no branch points in our reaction scheme, it is obvious that the rate of the whole reaction S → X will be the same as any partial reaction such as ES → X + E. In other words, we can consider the rate of the

* L. Michaelis and M. L. Menten, *Biochem. Z.*, **43**, 333 (1913).

total reaction, v, to be equal to the rate of the breakdown of ES in the direction of products. But in the fashion of Equation 1, this is given by

$$v = \frac{d[X]}{dt} = k_3[p] \qquad \text{(Eq. 3)}$$

Note that this reaction is given as irreversible. This simplifies things and is valid, since we shall consider the reaction only in fairly early stages, before much X has been produced and therefore before any back reaction is possible.

It is also extremely important (and interesting) to note that when one actually measures an enzyme reaction, it usually appears that the reaction proceeds at a constant rate for some time until the reactant begins to approach some sort of equilibrium. If this is so, it must be the case that the rate of the reaction ES → X must remain constant for a considerable period. This could not be so if the concentration of ES, $[p]$, were changing, since k_3 is a constant, in any case. Thus $[p]$ must also remain constant throughout much of the reaction, existing in a steady state, where the rate of formation of ES exactly equals its breakdown. This seemingly innocuous point turns out to have exciting consequences and leads directly to much of what we know about the general features of enzyme action.

For example, we see that, if ES is constant, the rate of the one reaction leading to its formation must exactly equal the sum of the two leading to its breakdown. Following the method in Equations 1 and 2, we can then write the following equation:

$$\text{Formation of ES} = \text{Breakdown of ES}$$
$$k_1[e - p][s] = k_2[p] + k_3[p]$$

and this can be written

$$k_1[es - ps] = [k_2 + k_3][p]$$

Then, dividing both sides by k_1,

$$es - ps = \left(\frac{k_2 + k_3}{k_1}\right)[p]$$

and, solving for es,

$$es = ps + \left(\frac{k_2 + k_3}{k_1}\right)[p]$$
$$= p\left[s + \left(\frac{k_2 + k_3}{k_1}\right)\right]$$

so that

$$p = \frac{es}{\dfrac{k_2 + k_3}{k_1}} + s \qquad \text{(Eq. 4)}$$

Now, we have already seen that the rate of the whole reaction, v, is the same as that of any segment and, most particularly, identical to that of the breakdown of the enzyme-substrate complex to form products. This was given in Equation 3 by

$$v = k_3[p]$$

If we substitute the value of p from Equation 4, this becomes

$$v = \frac{k_3 es}{\dfrac{k_2 + k_3}{k_1}} + s \qquad \text{(Eq. 5)}$$

This is a useful equation, giving rate as a function of a set of the constants k_1, k_2, and k_3, as well as the concentration of the enzyme and the substrate. However, it may be simplified by an additional consideration. Consider the case where the enzyme is saturated with substrate (far to the right on Figure 3–5). Under such conditions, the rate, v, might be said to approach a maximum value which we call V_{max}. The reason for this is that in the presence of excess substrate all the enzyme is in the form of the complex. In other words, as $s \to \infty$,

$$v \to V_{max}$$

because

$$p \to e$$

From this, it is clear that, substituting in Equation 3,

$$V_{max} = k_3[e]$$

which in turn may be substituted in Equation 5 to give

$$v = \frac{V_{max}[s]}{\dfrac{k_2 + k_3}{k_1}} + s \qquad \text{(Eq. 6)}$$

One further simplification in form may be gained by noting that the ratio of rate constants has passed through the derivation unaltered, in a way that enables us to group them together as a single constant which we call K_m, where

$$K_m = \frac{k_2 + k_3}{k_1}$$

Thus the basic enzyme equation, Equation 6, may be written

$$v = \frac{V_{\max}[s]}{K_m + [s]} \qquad \text{(Eq. 7)}$$

In addition, it turns out that K_m represents, not only a minor simplification of the equation, but that it has something of a life of its own. Equation 7 was derived by Michaelis and Menten from rather different postulates, among which was the definition of K_m as a dissociation constant for the enzyme-substrate complex to free enzyme and substrate. Although this view is generally invalid, they correctly noted that K_m provided a measure of "affinity" between the enzyme and the substrate molecule. The modern reader may wish to describe affinity in somewhat more chemical terms, but the fact is that K_m does provide a fair measure of the tightness of binding of the ES complex. Thus, together with $V_{\max}$, it provides a useful parameter for describing the action of a given enzyme, and a considerable part of the description of an enzyme involves the measurement of the two.

It might be thought that the evaluation of K_m requires the estimation of the individual rate constants. Fortunately, this is untrue, as rate constants for enzyme reactions are notoriously hard to get at. Likewise, the measurement of $V_{\max}$ would seem to involve direct measurement of rate at infinite substrate concentration, an approach which is often impossible for a variety of technical reasons.

Happily, a simple technique exists which yields both $V_{\max}$ and K_m from a single graphical presentation of the rate at various substrate concentrations. First, by simple algebra (the reader should check this) one may obtain a reciprocal form of equation 7, which becomes

$$\frac{1}{v} = \left(\frac{k_m}{V_{\max}}\right)\left(\frac{1}{[s]}\right) + \frac{1}{V_{\max}} \qquad \text{(Eq. 8)}$$

One may then plot data in the form of $1/v$ versus $1/s$, producing the graph shown in Figure 3–6. On this graph it is clear that at the $1/v$ axis

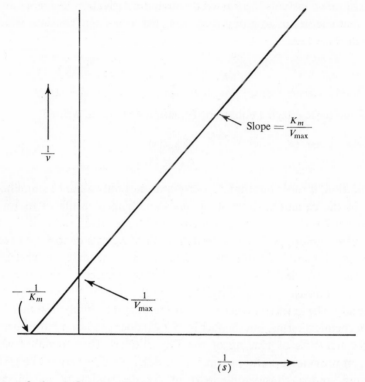

Figure 3–6.   *Influence of substrate concentration (s) on enzyme reaction rate, v. Plot of 1/v versus 1/(s), illustrating the method for estimating the maximum velocity, V_{max}, and the Michaelis constant, K_m.*

intercept, $1/s$ is 0, so that s must approach infinity. Thus $1/v$ becomes $1/V_{max}$. Furthermore, by elementary manipulation of Equation 8, it is seen that, when $1/v$ is 0 (the intercept with the $1/s$ axis), $1/s$ becomes $1/k_m$. Thus a set of relatively accessible measurements and a single graphical representation of data gives the two most important kinetic variables for an enzymic reaction.

Now, it is one thing to obtain kinetic measurements describing the activity of enzymes in a test tube and another to apply such results to the myriad enzymes of the living cell. It should be said here that the results obtained *in vitro* represent limiting cases for enzymes in their natural habitat—the cell. Thus, although the activity of an enzyme *in vivo* may be complicated by many things, it is unlikely to be inconsistent with the properties when studied using a pure, intact enzyme. Furthermore, the kinetic properties of pure enzymes are interesting from the point of view of understanding their cellular role. For example, K_m has been said to represent a sort of affinity between enzyme and substrate. If this be so, it is useful to know K_m's when one is trying to unravel such matters as competition of several enzymes for one substrate, since, all else being equal, the enzyme with the highest affinity will come out ahead.

Inhibition of enzymic reactions

There are a large number of ways to inhibit an enzymic reaction, including many which amount to destroying the enzyme. For example, the addition of strong acid will generally have an adverse effect, either by placing the protein in an unfriendly pH environment for activity or, even if the acid be at a high concentration, by hydrolyzing the protein. Furthermore, a number of reagents, including those which bind to the sulfhydryl groups of the protein, inhibit by blocking portions of the enzyme or by producing drastic changes in the tertiary structure of the enzyme. One might be tempted to assume that inhibition by a compound such as p-chloromercuribenzoate, which acts by binding to sulfhydryl groups, implies the presence of SH groups in the "active site" of the enzymes which it inhibits. Unfortunately, such an assumption is often untrue and, in fact, such inhibitors are of finite but limited usefulness. They frequently lack specificity, and in this provide a contrast to a second class of enzyme inhibitors, which are both interesting from the point of view of the study of enzyme action and important with regard to enzyme control mechanisms within the cell.

This extremely interesting set of enzyme inhibitors appears to act by virtue of their ability to compete with the substrate for the active site of the enzyme. In other words, the inhibitor is able to bind to the enzyme site (and has the equivalent of a K_m describing this binding) but is unchanged by the enzyme. The reaction sequence for the normal action of the enzyme on its substrate

$$E + S \rightleftharpoons ES \longrightarrow P$$

becomes, in the case of the inhibitor I,

$$E + I \rightleftharpoons EI$$

Since the two reactions of E (with S and I) are in competition, they will be affected both by the affinities between the enzyme and S and I, and by the relative concentrations of the two compounds. If one adds some inhibitors and obtains, perhaps, 50 per cent inhibition, it is possible to add more substrate and reduce the inhibition to a lower value. In this case, adding more substrate enables it to compete more effectively for a place on the enzyme surface, a possibility reflected in the common term for such effects as *competitive inhibition*.

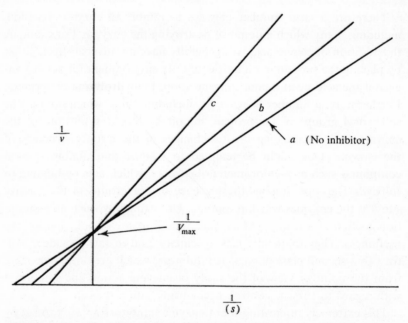

Figure 3–7. *The effect of a competitive inhibitor on enzyme reaction rate. Lines b and c represent the rate with increasing concentrations of a competitive inhibitor. Note that such inhibitors do not alter V_{max}.*

There is an interesting corollary to the ability to reverse competitive inhibition with excess substrate. Since by adding enough substrate one can, in principle, reverse inhibition completely, a competitive inhibitor cannot be said to alter the maximum velocity V_{max} of a reaction. For this reason, a plot of $1/v$ versus $1/s$ gives characteristic results in the case of a competitive inhibitor and can be used to identify such inhibition. Figure 3–7 shows a family of lines representing various inhibitor concentrations, all of which pass through a common value for $1/V_{max}$, all with different apparent Michaelis constants, as shown by $1/K_m$. This is entirely in keeping with our remarks about K_m, representing a measure of affinity between enzyme and substrate, since a second molecule competing at the active site would certainly alter the affinity of that site from the point of view of the substrate (it would tend to gum it up).

Since one of the most significant features of enzymes is their enormous specificity, the existence of molecules other than the substrate which may be bound to the site of activity suggests the possibility of probing the geometry of the site. Indeed, a survey of competitive inhibitors shows that, in nearly all cases, the inhibitor bears a very close structural similarity to the substrate molecule. For example, the enzyme succinate dehydrogenase acts by withdrawing two electrons from carbons 2 and 3 of succinate and passing them to the respiratory chain (see Chapter 6). Succinate is converted by this action to fumarate as follows:

$$
\begin{array}{ccc}
\text{COOH} & & \text{COOH} \\
| & & | \\
\text{CH}_2 & & \text{CH} \\
| & \longrightarrow & \| \\
\text{CH}_2 & & \text{HC} \\
| & & | \\
\text{COOH} & & \text{HOOC}
\end{array}
\quad + \ 2e \ + \ 2H^+
$$

$$\text{Succinate} \qquad \text{Fumarate}$$

Now, it is interesting that a potent competitive inhibitor of this reaction is the dicarboxylic acid, malonate, which is seen to bear a striking resemblance to the substrate. On examination of the structure of malonate,

$$
\begin{array}{c}
\text{COOH} \\
| \\
\text{CH}_2 \\
| \\
\text{COOH}
\end{array}
$$

$$\text{Malonate}$$

one is tempted to say that its symmetrical geometry with the two carboxyl groups makes it look very like succinate to the enzyme, but the lack of a second CH_2 makes withdrawal of the two electrons impossible, and therefore blocks any possible reaction leading to a reaction product. In other words, the formation of half a double bond makes very little sense. Although malonate is a potent and exhaustively studied inhibitor of the reaction, it is interesting that a number of other inhibitors exist, including, among others, the following:

$$
\begin{array}{cccc}
COOH & COOH & COOH & COOH \\
| & | & | & | \\
C{=}O & CH & CH & CH_2 \\
| & \| & \| & | \\
CH_2 & HC & CH & C{=}O \\
| & | & | & | \\
COOH & HOOC & COOH & CH_3 \\
\text{Oxaloacetate} & \text{Fumarate} & \text{Maleate} & \text{Acetoacetate}
\end{array}
$$

Of these, the most effective is oxaloacetate, which has a greater binding capability than even malonate, whereas acetoacetate is less effective by a factor of about 10 than any of the others. This might be taken to indicate that two carboxyl groups are required for really effective binding to the active region of succinate dehydrogenase, a conclusion for which there is considerable evidence.

It is also very interesting that two of the competitive inhibitors of the enzyme are the product, fumarate, and its isomer, maleate. Indeed, the observation that the product of an enzyme reaction inhibits the reaction is a general one. A large number of such cases have been demonstrated and described as *product inhibition*. The discovery of competitive inhibition by a product should not be very surprising, since there are very few enzymes that produce such a radical structural change in their substrate that the product looks too drastically different from the substrate. In other words, products tend to look somewhat like the substrates and so might be expected to inhibit.

In addition, it should be emphasized that product inhibition, as in all competitive inhibition, is the result of binding of inhibitor to the enzyme surface. It is not identical to the much more general "inhibition" that occurs in any reaction where the product builds up. The latter case represents nothing more than an approach to equilibrium with consequent decrease in reaction velocity.

The widespread occurrence of product inhibition is also interesting from the point of view of cellular control of chemical reactions. The economy of the cell is such that reactions are usually allowed to proceed only as fast as the product may be utilized in still other reactions. Product inhibition provides a partial means whereby reactions do not exceed the requirements placed on them by the cell, in that, when the product builds up to an excessive level, the reaction tends to be inhibited. This example of negative feedback has an added feature of competitive inhibition—that inhibition is minimal, as long as the substrate is in excess compared to the product. Thus the reaction is able to approach the correct level very quickly before regulation by product inhibition takes place, a feature which is of considerable importance in maintaining responsive, but highly controlled, metabolic pathways in the cell.

End-product inhibition

Not only may control of an individual reaction be exerted by means of product inhibition, a form of competitive inhibition, but mechanisms exist where the final product of a metabolic sequence inhibits a reaction near the beginning of that sequence. Consider a synthetic pathway proceeding from compound A via several intermediates, B, C, and D, to the finished product:

$$A \longrightarrow B \longrightarrow C \longrightarrow D \longrightarrow Product$$

A number of instances are known where such a pathway is inhibited by the product, but rather than the inhibition taking place between D and the product, as in the case of ordinary product inhibition, it occurs at an earlier site, often between A and B. Thus, if the product is available to the cell (say in the diet), its synthesis is inhibited, as is that of intermediates leading to it. However, there are many cases where intermediates are shared by several pathways. In the example above, compound B might well lead to the synthesis of two amino acids by a branched pathway:

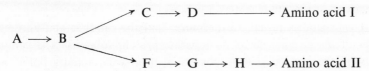

In this scheme, an excess of amino acid I would not necessarily imply that the synthesis of amino acid II should be shut off, and therefore it would be unfortunate if a common portion of the pathway such as the A → B reaction should be the site of end-product inhibition. In fact, as a rule, this difficulty is avoided, and reactions are inhibited by the final product only on the unique pathway leading to it. In our hypothetical example, amino acid II would be most likely to inhibit reactions from B to amino acid II only, and not those leading to the formation of amino acid I.

It seems clear the end-product inhibition does not occur by means of simple product (or competitive) inhibition. For one thing, the structure of the end product is less likely to resemble that of an early precursor. Likewise, the specificity of inhibition in branched pathways suggests a different sort of mechanism. In fact, it appears that enzymes which are inhibited in this manner possess two sites on the enzyme surface, one concerned with the activity of the enzyme, the other a site of attachment for the end-product inhibitor. The binding of the end product to the inhibitory site produces changes in the tertiary structure of the enzyme which, in turn, alter the reactivity of the catalytic portion of the enzyme molecule. The noncatalytic site of inhibitor binding has come to be called the *allosteric site* of the enzyme, and enzymes with such an arrangement—consequently subject to end-product inhibition—are known as *allosteric enzymes.*

A good example of such an allosteric enzyme is aspartate trans-carbamylase, which is on the pathway leading to the formation of cytidine triphosphate (CTP). Activity of the enzyme is inhibited by the pathway's end product, CTP, which is structurally quite unrelated to the substrate of the enzyme, aspartate. Apparently there are two sites on the enzyme surface, one carrying out catalysis and the other involved in regulation by CTP. This is suggested by the ability of the sulfhydryl-binding inhibitor, *p*-chloromercuribenzoate, to eliminate control by CTP, even though it does not inhibit the activity of the enzyme (when CTP is absent). It appears that *p*-chloromercuribenzoate inhibits the binding of CTP to the allosteric site but does not influence directly the reactivity of the site where catalysis occurs.

Recent studies reveal, furthermore, that the catalytic and allosteric sites of the enzyme occur on separate protein subunits. The subunit bearing the catalytic site is possessed of enzymic activity but is not subject to regulation by CTP. The subunit bearing the CTP-binding site is devoid of activity but, when mixed in correct proportions with the catalytic subunit, confers on it the property of allosteric regulation by CTP.

Coupled enzyme systems

It is all too clear that much of what has been said thus far in this chapter is rigorously applicable only to isolated single enzymes under the best conditions. The situation in the cell is much more complex and, although some properties of purified enzymes (for example, product inhibition) are obviously applicable to the intact cell, others are less clearly so. Although a discussion of the role of enzymes in metabolism in subsequent chapters will put considerable flesh on the bones of pure enzyme chemistry, at this stage it is worth making several observations about enzyme-mediated pathways in general.

Consider a general pathway

$$A \xrightarrow{1} B \xrightarrow{2} C \xrightarrow{3} C \xrightarrow{4} \text{etc.}$$

where it is clear that the rate of each reaction will be, in part, determined by the others. The substrate for reaction 2 is the product of reaction 1, so the rate of 2 may be directly related to the progress of 1. Furthermore, if reaction 2 is inhibited by its product, its rate will also be regulated by the third reaction, which will be engaged in removing that product. Real metabolic pathways are still more involved, with branches and sundry other complications, and the complete description of a pathway in terms of steady-state enzyme kinetics, where every velocity is a function of all the other velocities, gives rise to exceedingly unpleasant mathematics. Fortunately, nature sometimes simplifies things a bit, such as in cases where one reaction is so much slower than the others that it can be regarded as rate-limiting. However, there is usually no easy way out and the sum of a number of enzymic reactions which can be treated rigorously when taken singly, together must be examined in a relatively crude fashion, often being regarded not so much in terms of molecular kinetics as a sort of analogy to fluid flow.

Suggested Reading

ANFINSEN, C. B., *The Molecular Basis of Evolution*, John Wiley & Sons, New York, 1959.

DIXON, M., and E. C. WEBB, *Enzymes*, Academic Press, New York, 2nd ed., 1964.

EDSALL, J. T., and J. WYMAN, *Biophysical Chemistry*, Vol. 1, Academic Press, New York, 1958, Chap. 3.

FRUTON, J. S., and S. SIMMONDS, *General Biochemistry*, John Wiley & Sons, New York, 2nd ed., 1958, Chap. 2–5.

INTERNATIONAL UNION OF BIOCHEMISTRY, *Enzyme Nomenclature*, Elsevier, New York, 1965.

MEISTER, A., *Biochemistry of the Amino Acids*, Vols. I and II, Academic Press, New York, 2nd ed., 1965.

NEILANDS, J. B., and P. K. STUMPF, *Outlines of Enzyme Chemistry*, John Wiley & Sons, New York, 2nd ed., 1958.

PERUTZ, M. F., *Proteins and Nucleic Acids*, Elsevier, New York, 1962.

STADTMAN, E. R., "Allosteric regulation of enzyme activity," in *Advances in Enzymology*, F. F. Nord (ed.), Vol. 28, Interscience, New York, 1966.

CHAPTER 4

Regulation of Enzyme Synthesis

It is clear from Chapter 3 that the nature of catalytic action by enzymes allows control of enzyme activity by the concentration of substrate and products. The rates of enzymic reactions within cells appear under significant control by such mechanisms, and product inhibition, which is a special case of competitive inhibition, is surely important in preventing the buildup of impossible concentrations of any one product. However, since product inhibition is unlikely to lead to a complete shutting off of an unnecessary pathway, its level of control must be more in the nature of a fine adjustment of the flow through the various pathways. When the cell must exercise a more total control over its chemical activities, it is clear that other, more decisive, mechanisms must operate and it develops that such mechanisms exist and have to do with enzyme synthesis.

Consider the case of a cell which is able to make a certain compound, such as a coenzyme, which is necessary for its growth. The pathway for its synthesis must be intact as long as the cell has no other source of the coenzyme. However, if the cell is suddenly placed in a situation where the coenzyme is available—say, through nutrition—then the pathway is at once irrelevant and wasteful, in that it siphons off compounds perhaps useful elsewhere. Cells, living in most instances, poised on the brink of metabolic disaster, cannot exist with very much wastefulness, and it should be no surprise that controls exist to prevent it.

In addition, consider the case of a cell (perhaps a bacterium) able to grow using a wide variety of compounds as sources of carbon and energy. The range of compounds might well include a dozen or so sugars, several amino acids, organic acids, hydrocarbons, etc. However, out of the impressive variety of possibilities, the cell often uses only one at a time for the simple reason that only one is likely to be available in a given ecological situation. Although the cell is using one compound for its energy or carbon source, it must still possess the capability to use all the others at some time in the future. If the cell were to contain the enzymes necessary for assimiliation of all of the compounds, it would be carrying about and synthesizing a large mass of enzyme protein completely without benefit to itself, at the time. The synthesis of enzymes for which no substrate is available represents an extreme sort of wastefulness and, again, cells tend to avoid wastefulness, in order to survive. Again, a mechanism does exist in many cells to avoid the synthesis of unnecessary enzymes while maintaining the potential ability to make enzymes in the future when the need arises.

Induced enzymes

For many years, cases have been known where the presence of a certain enzymatic activity depends upon the prior exposure of the organism to its substrate. For example, early in this century a fungus was found that could hydrolyze the disaccharide, sucrose, only when the organism had been previously grown in its presence. Enzymes that are synthesized only in response to the presence of their substrate have come to be called *induced enzymes*, and those which are not thus inducible (those synthesized equally well in the presence or absence of substrate) are called *constitutive*. At the present time there is great research interest in induced enzymes, not only because of their obvious role in the regulation of cell metabolism, but also because they represent a nongenetic response to the environment, with obvious overtones in the area of cell differentiation. In addition, induced enzymes have turned out to be very interesting from the point of view of studying protein synthesis, as they represent an opportunity to turn the synthesis of a specific protein on or off at will.

Much of our present knowledge about induced enzymes comes from the elegant studies carried out by workers at L'Institut Pasteur in Paris over the past two decades. This work has largely centered on one organism, *Escherichia coli*, and one enzyme, β-galactosidase. Although this is only one of many known induced enzymes, knowledge of it is more complete than in other cases, and we shall use it as our example for the class of induced enzymes as a whole. The action of β-galactosidase involves the hydrolysis of a β-galactoside, of which the best known example is lactose. Under the influence of the enzyme, lactose is hydrolyzed to yield one molecule each of glucose and galactose:

The presence of the enzyme enables *E. coli* to use lactose as a carbon and energy source and so is obviously required for growth when other carbon compounds are lacking. When cells in which β-galactosidase is inducible are grown in the absence of lactose, no enzyme is formed. Then, when the cells are placed in a new medium in which lactose is the sole carbon and energy source, growth is seen to resume only after a considerable lag period (Figure 4–1). During this time, it appears that the cells are synthesizing β-galactosidase and must make a finite amount of it before lactose may be used and growth begins.

When such experiments were first performed, there were few prior instances where cell metabolism was affected by external factors in a nongenetic (temporary) way and explanations were sought to explain the results in terms of selection. Thus it was said that the action of "inducer" was really to select for those few β-galactosidase-containing cells in the population, enabling them to grow to the exclusion of the others. Such selection would appear to the external observer as if lactose were stimulating the production of the enzyme, whereas actually it was

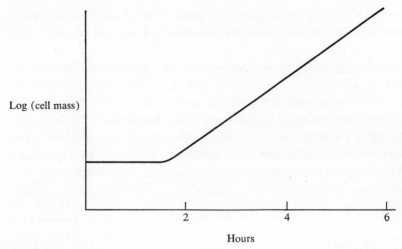

Figure 4–1. *Lag period in growth of* E. coli *resulting from induction of β-galactosidase.*

only selecting for those cells that had the enzyme already. This ambiguity was resolved by the discovery of compounds which could induce activity of the enzyme while not serving as either its substrate or as a carbon source for the cell. It was found that thiomethylgalactoside (TMG),

was able to stimulate the formation of β-galactosidase activity in a cell population without being metabolized by the cell, thus providing no selective advantage for cells already containing the enzyme. In this fashion it became clear that the inducer acted by directly stimulating the synthesis of the enzyme and not by any form of selection. Such enzymic induction, where the inducing compound is unused by the cell, is called *gratuitous induction*, and has proved to be an especially valuable means for studying the inductive process.

Thus it is clear that the ability of a cell to utilize a particular compound is a complex affair, depending on the genetic ability of the cell to make the requisite enzyme in the first place, and the capacity of the cell to respond to induction in the second. The ability to make the enzyme is, strictly speaking, a genetic matter; the inductive process is more of the nature of phenotypic expression of the genetic makeup of the cell.

An additional sort of control is superimposed on these, as cells have been isolated which may be shown to possess the genetic information for β-galactosidase synthesis, have normal inductive processes, but are quite unable to grow with lactose as the sole carbon source. Further study of such organisms shows that the problem lies with the failure of the sugar to penetrate to the interior of the cell, where the enzyme exists in the soluble phase of the cytoplasm. Clearly, a permeation mechanism, allowing entry of the sugar, is lacking in such cells. This may be demonstrated by the presence of β-galactosidase activity in cells which have been treated to disrupt the permeability barrier or by untreated cells in the presence of very high concentrations of lactose, in which some sugar is formed inside by ordinary diffusion.

Thus if one discovers that a certain population of cells is unable to break down lactose (or whatever), there are three separate matters to consider. First, the cells may simply lack the genetic information required to synthesize β-galactosidase. Second, even if they carry the information for the enzyme synthesis, they may have been grown in the absence of inducer, and hence lack the enzyme. Finally, they may contain active enzyme, which is inoperative, owing to lack of substrate permeation.

Just as there are three separate questions concerning the ability of cells to use lactose, there are three separate genetic loci involving such activity. Figure 4–2 shows a segment of the *E. coli* genetic map concerned with β-galactosidase activity. The reader is referred to any textbook of modern genetics for a detailed discussion of the genetics of induced enzymes. Here it is sufficient to note that the three loci are quite closely linked—they tend to be grouped together in a recombination experiment—and that they are quite independent in their ability to mutate. In the figure, y represents the locus controlling the permeation of lactose into the cell. The physiology of such permeation will be discussed in Chapter 8; here we shall only say that $y+$ means that the permeation mechanism is intact in the cell, $y-$ that it is lacking. The locus denoted z is the *structural locus*, carrying the information needed for the actual synthesis of the enzyme galactosidase. If the cell lacks the information (is $z-$), the enzyme cannot be produced, no matter what the other loci are. Finally, i represents the inducibility locus such

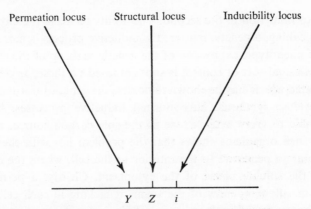

Figure 4–2. *The β-galactosidase region of the* E. coli *genetic map.*

that $i+$ is the inducible case and $i-$ that of a constitutive enzyme. Note that, since all loci mutate independently, there are eight possible configurations at the three sites ($y+$, $z+$, $i-$), but that only one of these configurations leads to activity in absence of inducer. Note also that, of the three loci, only one is "classical" in the sense of being simply information for the synthesis of an ordinary protein (see Chapter 11). The interpretation of the other two is of fundamental interest and is discussed below.

Repression of enzyme synthesis

We have seen that the growth of cells in the presence of a compound can lead to the production of enzymes required for its utilization, a device enabling cells to make only the enzymes needed under existing environmental conditions. This sort of control is exerted at the *beginning* of a metabolic chain of reactions, enabling the cell to utilize an external source of material for the synthesis of required cell components (Figure 4–3).

In addition, a second species of control exists in cell metabolism, which is sort of a mirror image of enzyme induction and which prevents a cell from synthesizing components rendered unnecessary by their presence in the extracellular medium. For example, a cell may be able to synthesize enzymes leading to the production of an amino acid or, say, a purine, which are required by the cell for growth and viability. These enzymes are required only as long as there is no other source of the amino acid or purine. However, when the compound exists in the

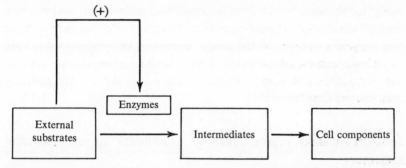

Figure 4–3. *Regulation of cell metabolism by induced enzymes. The* (+) *indicates that the substrate of an induced enzyme* stimulates *its production.*

medium, it is no longer necessary for the cell to make it, and, in fact, the continued synthesis of the compound becomes redundant and wasteful. Clearly an additional means of regulation is advantageous.

The control of synthesis of enzymes of a metabolic sequence by the final product is widespread and is known as *enzyme repression*. It is summarized in Figure 4–4, which should be compared to Figure 4–3,

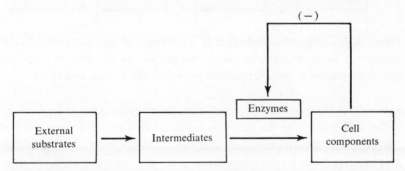

Figure 4–4. *Regulation of cell metabolism by enzyme repression. The* (−) *sign indicates that the final product* inhibits *synthesis of the enzymes that are subject to repression.*

which deals with induced enzymes. It is very important to remember that enzyme repression is the repression of enzyme *synthesis*, and not activity, as in the case of product inhibition. Control of enzyme synthesis tends to yield a much more total control, and, as we said, regulation of enzyme activity is a kind of fine adjustment. On the other hand, the response of a pathway to the inhibition of activity by a product is likely to be more rapid than a repression mechanism, which often depends on dilution of existing enzyme by means of cell growth without new enzyme synthesis. In this sense, repression of synthesis takes care of the long-term metabolic needs of the cell, while inhibition may smooth out fluctuations and keep material flowing evenly through the pathway over shorter time intervals.

Induction and repression of synthesis of an enzyme sequence

Since cells are generally involved in the control of a whole pathway, and not merely of a single enzyme, it is desirable to examine the action of repression and induction on the group of enzymes concerned with sequential synthesis (Figure 4–5). In the case of the induction of a

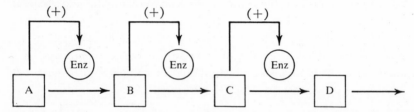

Figure 4–5. *Sequential induction of a pathway. A pathway mediated by a chain of induced enzymes allows the product of the first reaction to induce formation of the enzyme that promotes the second, and so on.*

pathway, it is sometimes observed that the enzymes are synthesized in order, with the first in the pathway being the first made. The reason for the sequential appearance of the enzymes is simply that induction of the first enzyme leads to the accumulation of its product, which, in turn, leads to induction of the second enzyme, and so on.

Repression of an enzyme sequence appears to result from the separate repression of each of the enzymes of the sequence under the influence of the end product. As in the case of allosteric enzyme inhibition, branched pathways require more complex repression mechanisms. Figure 4–6 illustrates two situations in which a branched metabolic sequence places special requirements on repression as an effective control. In one instance, repression extends only to those enzymes in the portion of the pathway leading uniquely to the repressor. In the other, repression of synthesis of enzymes prior to a branch point only takes

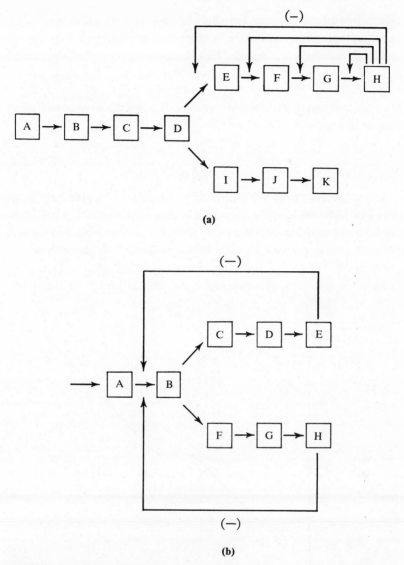

Figure 4-6. *Repression of the synthesis of enzymes involved in a branched pathway. In the simple case* (a), *repression only extends as far as the branch. Part* (b) *illustrates "polyvalent" repression, where* all *final products are required to prevent synthesis of an enzyme located prior to the branch point. In both cases, the letters denote metabolic intermediates and the short arrows, reactions mediated by enzymes. A minus sign indicates inhibition.*

place when *all* end products have built up to a certain level, a mechanism ensuring that repression by one of them does not lead to a deficiency in the product of another branch. This last pattern of repression is called *multivalent repression*. It is also interesting to note that genetic studies often show that the loci for enzymes under the control of one repressor are clustered together on the chromosome. The significance of such close genetic linkage will be discussed later.

Selective utilization of metabolic routes

When bacterial cells are grown on a medium containing two metabolizable substrates, including glucose and any one of a number of other compounds, a characteristic growth curve is obtained with a marked inflection and lag period in the middle. This *diauxic* curve is illustrated in Figure 4–7 and appears to be the result of one of the compounds (in this case, glucose) repressing the utilization of the other.

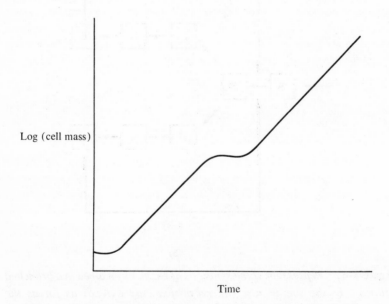

Figure 4–7. *Diauxic growth. Cells of* E. coli *are grown on a mixture of two carbon sources, including glucose and glycerol. The population grows, using glucose until it is exhausted. At that time, repression by glucose of the enzymes required for glycerol metabolism ceases and, after a short lag period, growth resumes with glycerol as substrate.*

In the first part of the curve, growth takes place with glucose as the sole carbon and energy source, and enzymes for the utilization of the other substrate are repressed. When the cells run out of glucose, enzymes connected with glycerol uptake are lacking but may now be synthesized, accounting for the lag period. Finally, growth resumes using glycerol. This phenomenon may be regarded as a case where the cell selects one of two available metabolic pathways—presumably the most favorable one from the point of view of metabolic efficiency. The exact mechanism of this glucose effect remains unclear, although it may involve inhibition in the transfer of the second compound across the cell membrane when glucose is present.

The mechanism of induction and repression

Obviously, the synthesis of an enzyme, whether induced or constitutive, is a special case of protein synthesis, which will be discussed explicitly in Chapter 11. However, there are comments that may be made about induced (and repressed) enzyme synthesis without reference to the details of protein synthesis which give some insight as to how regulation tends to occur in cells. There are two questions concerning mechanism which are of central interest to us here:

1. In the case of enzyme induction, does the inducer stimulate enzyme production in a direct way, or does it lead to the removal of an internal repressor? Note that if the latter is true, induction and repression are two facets of the same event. Note also that the reverse might also be true— that induction might be the primary action, and that repression might result from the removal of an internal inducer. These two possibilities are summarized in Figure 4–8. The second question, obviously related to this, is

2. Is a cellular enzyme constitutive because an internal repressor is lacking, or perhaps because the protein-synthesizing machinery of the cell is insensitive to the inducer?

A partial answer to both questions came from elegant mating experiments using E. coli, where it was shown that the cytoplasm of cells in which β-galactosidase was inducible contained an internal repressor molecule which was synthesized by the cell. In other words, the $i+$ (inducible) locus appeared to be involved in the synthesis of an internal repressor which could be bound, destroyed, or otherwise eliminated by

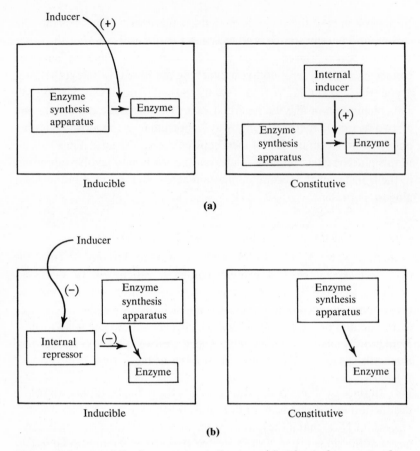

Figure 4–8. *Models for enzyme induction.* (a) *The inducer stimulates enzyme production in a direct way. A cell which is constitutive for a certain enzyme, then, contains an internal inducer.* (b) *In the second model, the role of the inducer is to eliminate an internal repressor. According to this view, cells which fail to make the repressor are constitutive.*

the addition of the inducer. The constitutive state $i-$ would lack the ability to form the repressor. Clearly, this result leads to the conclusion that induction and repression are two aspects of a single repression mechanism which lead to the regulation of enzyme synthesis by small molecules.

Although this view of the control of enzyme synthesis, summarized in Figure 4–9, is supported by considerable experimental evidence, it must be said that an internal repressor has not yet been isolated. Since such

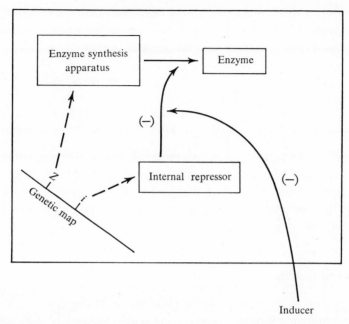

Figure 4–9. *Regulation of enzyme synthesis by means of an internal repressor. The role of an inducer is to prevent repression. In the case of β-galactosidase in* E. coli, *information for enzyme synthesis is provided by the structural locus Z and that for repressor synthesis at the inducibility i locus.*

compounds probably act at extremely low concentrations, failure to obtain repressor in pure form can hardly be said to argue against the theory. In any case, more detailed versions of the mechanism illustrated in Figure 4–9 have been proposed and have led to interesting experimental approaches (which is what mechanisms are for). The study of enzymic induction and repression is now one of the more active areas of cell biology, both for its own interest and because of its fundamental importance in any area of biology where regulation by environmental conditions is important.

Control of enzyme synthesis in higher organisms

Most of the experiments leading to our present views of enzyme regulation have been carried out using microorganisms. This is not to say that enzyme regulation is unknown or irrelevant in multicellular organisms; indeed, many cases of it have been described. Because of ambiguities associated with the interpretation of induction experiments using intact multicellular organisms, some of the most interesting cases of induced enzymes in mammalian cells have been described in cells grown in pure culture. For example, the enzyme glutamine synthetase, which catalyzes the reaction

$$\text{Glutamate} + NH_3 + ATP \rightleftharpoons \text{Glutamine} + ADP + \text{phosphate}$$

has been shown to be repressed in a mammalian cell culture by a product of the reaction, glutamine. The increasing number of cases of enzyme induction and repression which are being studied in higher cells indicates clearly that the phenomena are general and of central importance in the metabolic life of such organisms.

Suggested Reading

Cold Spring Harbor Symposia on Quantitative Biology, Vol. XXVIII, "Synthesis and Structure of Macromolecules," Long Island Biological Association, Cold Spring Harbor, N. Y., 1963.

VOGEL, H. J., V. BRYSON, and J. O. LAMPEN (eds.), *Informational Macromolecules*, Part V, Academic Press, New York, 1963.

WATSON, J. D., *Molecular Biology of the Gene*, W. A. Benjamin, New York, 1965, Chap. 14.

CHAPTER 5

Enzyme Systems

The chemical transformations which take place within cells are known, collectively, as *metabolism*. Most of what a cell does is closely related to one or more chemical reactions, so metabolism is at the heart of much of cell physiology. Likewise, the techniques which cells have evolved for the control of metabolism are the basis for control of almost all other cellular events as well, and their study is of obvious interest.

A complete discussion of metabolism should include an exposition of all the chemical pathways of the cell, as well as their control and interrelations. Since our knowledge of their control and interrelations is somewhat incomplete in many instances, and since a complete catalog of metabolic reactions or pathways would fill a number of volumes, we shall follow a more modest course, the examination of a few pathways which seem to be quite pivotal. For example, the pathway (known as *glycolysis*) involving the breakdown of glucose is involved in a fundamental way in energy conversion, and also in the synthesis of many components, since a number of pathways branch off from it at various points. We will thus follow glucose breakdown, partly because it illustrates a number of features of metabolic pathways in general, and partly because it is itself at the heart of many metabolic sequences.

75

Techniques of metabolic studies

To discuss any metabolic pathway in a rational manner, it is necessary to consider how such a pathway may be examined experimentally, since the nature of our knowledge about such matters depends very much on the route by which we gained it. Furthermore, the student of cell biology often deals with metabolic pathways only as rather confusing sequences of organic formulas on paper, a vision of cell life which must be quite dull and which obscures the sense of game and strategy that permeates such areas of cell study.

The examination of metabolism may be conveniently divided into two basic strategies, both of which are generally required for a complete understanding of what is going on. They are (1) examination of the flow of compounds through intact pathways, and (2) the resolution of the pathways into individual enzymic reactions. The ideal confirmation of the validity of a biochemical pathway is the reconstitution of the pathway from the individual enzymes, although unfortunately this is not always possible (or even attempted).

Study of intact pathways

Techniques used in studying the flow of material through a pathway are dependent on the number of ways in which intermediates of the pathway may be measured. Ideally, a method should be used which allows continuous estimation of the concentration of reactants, although this is not always feasible.

Probably the most useful type of determination in the study of metabolism is spectrophotometric. For example, one may follow the progress of many biochemical reactions by watching changes in the absorption of light, either in the visible, ultraviolet, or infrared region of the spectrum. Consider the reaction

$$\text{Substrate} + \text{NAD}^+ \xrightarrow{\text{dehydrogenase}} \text{Oxydized substrate} + \text{NADH} + \text{H}^+$$

In this case, NADH (the reduced form of nicotinamide adenine dinucleotide, an important coenzyme) has a strong absorption peak in the ultraviolet region at 340 mμ while NAD$^+$ has none. Therefore, the progress of the reaction may be followed continuously by watching the increase in absorbance at 340 mμ, using a standard visible-ultraviolet spectrophotometer. Such a technique obviously depends on the absence of changes at 340 mμ due to other substances, a restriction which usually presents little difficulty. Other forms of spectroscopic measurement used in the study of metabolism include nuclear magnetic resonance spectroscopy (of value in the study of reactions involving free radicals), and spectrophotometry utilizing rapid-flow techniques which make it possible to follow reactions over periods as short as a few thousandths of a second.

A valuable nonspectrophotometric method is manometry, where changes in gas pressure (or volume) are followed. Manometric techniques are especially important in the reactions of respiration (which involve oxygen uptake) or photosynthesis (which involve oxygen evolution). In addition, reactions are often measured by means of polarography (which can also be applied to estimation of oxygen-consuming or producing reactions) and changes in hydrogen ion, which are often part of biological reactions and are easily followed by means of a glass-electrode pH meter.

Any of the methods described above may be used under appropriate conditions to follow the course of a pathway by examining the disappearance of the initial substrate or the increase in the final product. It is more difficult to dissect the sequence into its parts, but such tricks as the use of inhibitors may often be successful. A metabolic inhibitor which disrupts a pathway may often be useful, as one may detect the buildup of the compound just on the input side of the site of inhibition as the inhibitor dams up the flow. Examples of the importance of inhibition studies will be given later in the context of cell respiration.

Radioisotopes provide an important technique for the elucidation of pathways, and several strategies have been especially successful. In the simplest case, it is often possible to obtain radioactive samples of the starting compound in a metabolic series and, after adding them to cells or whatever is being studied, to isolate labeled intermediate compounds by chromatographic techniques, after which they may be measured by means of Geiger counting. The rate of appearance of radioactivity in these compounds is especially important, since the high degree of interconnection between metabolic systems makes almost anything radioactive from almost any labeled precursor, if one waits long enough. It is thus important that the compounds thought to be in a metabolic

(a) Direct Incorporation

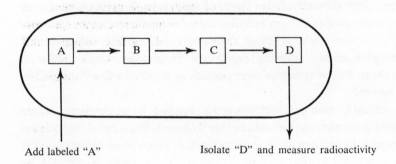

Add labeled "A"   Isolate "D" and measure radioactivity

(b) Isotopic Competition

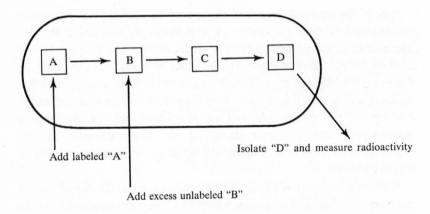

Add labeled "A"

Isolate "D" and measure radioactivity

Add excess unlabeled "B"

Figure 5–1.   *Isotopic methods in the study of metabolic pathways.* (a) *Direct incorporation experiment, where one determines whether addition of a labeled hypothetical precursor leads to rapid labeling of the product.* (b) *Isotopic competition. In order to see if " B " is on the pathway between " A " and " D " measure the rate of labeling of " D " with and without added cold " B." If " B " is an intermediate, then cold " B " will suppress labeling of " D."*

sequence be rapidly labeled and the rate of labeling should be consistent with the rate of flow through the pathway (if it is known).

A second and very valuable experimental approach to the study of pathways by tracers is that of isotopic competition. This method involves the addition of labeled precursor and measurement of the radioactivity of the final product. If one suspects that a certain compound is an intermediate in the series, the addition of cold (unlabeled) compound should depress the incorporation of label into the final product. This technique is summarized in Figure 5–1.

Finally, a technique of the greatest importance in metabolic study has been the use of biochemically blocked mutants of microorganisms. This technique, which has led to the description of a number of biosynthetic pathways, involves the isolation of a number of different mutants, all unable to synthesize the compound whose synthetic route is to be studied. If one examines mutants unable to synthesize compound E according to the pathway

$$A \longrightarrow B \longrightarrow C \longrightarrow D \longrightarrow E$$

an organism blocked between B and C will probably make an abnormally large amount of B and no E. In addition, since the pathway between C and E is intact, the addition of C will enable the organism to make E in a normal fashion. The examination of a number of such mutants blocked in different places leads to knowledge of the complete series, which may then be checked by other means. It is important to note that in all such investigations the worker is greatly assisted by a knowledge of the organic chemical mechanisms which are likely to lead to the final product, so that he does not have to examine an infinite number of possible pathways. Cells, in other words, may be expected to obey the normal rules of organic chemistry.

The resolution of a metabolic sequence into individual reactions

The first stage in the fractionation of the machinery by which the cell makes something is essentially a problem in protein purification. It is very important that the individual enzymes be really pure, inasmuch as impure enzymes often have a number of different activities that lead to wild and unreliable results in the study of metabolism. (The reader is urged to refer to any textbook of biochemistry for the techniques of enzyme purification.) Suffice it to say here that useful techniques include salt fractionation, where proteins are separated by their differing solubility in solutions of such a salt as ammonium sulfate. Various forms of chromatography are of central importance in protein and therefore enzyme fractionation, including ion-exchange column chromatography as well as electrophoretic separation on paper and thin-layer plates. All such approaches depend on varying affinities between different proteins and the material in the column or paper or the surface of the thin-layer plate. Devices are available that collect samples of material as they come from a column and record the amount of protein in each sample, a refinement of great benefit, as a single chromatographic separation may take a number of hours.

Other means of purification include electrophoresis, which is the placing of a sample in a field of high voltage. Proteins may thus be separated on the basis of their charge and additional resolution may often be obtained by changing the pH under which electrophoresis is carried out, thereby altering the charge due to the free ionizable groups of the protein. Finally, the technique of centrifugation is important in enzyme separations, inasmuch as a number of enzymes are found as aggregates large enough to be sedimented in a high centrifugal field.

Figure 5–2 summarizes enzyme purification techniques by showing how a hypothetical enzyme might be isolated from cell material. At each stage of the purification, the activity of the enzyme is determined as a measure of how much enzyme there is, and recorded as total and specific activity, the latter expressed as activity per weight, giving a measure of purity.

The real test of a proposed metabolic pathway is the reconstitution of the pathway from known enzymes, each isolated by such techniques as described above. This is a difficult and time-consuming affair and has been done in only a limited number of cases. Figure 5–3 is a somewhat simplified version of a reconstituted system which served as confirmation of a reconstituted system which served as confirmation of a number of the reactions of glycolysis (the degradation of glucose) and also as a useful analytic method for the determination of an important compound, adenosine triphosphate (ATP).

The technique consists in mixing a sample containing ATP (which is, itself, quite difficult to measure directly) with excess glucose and the

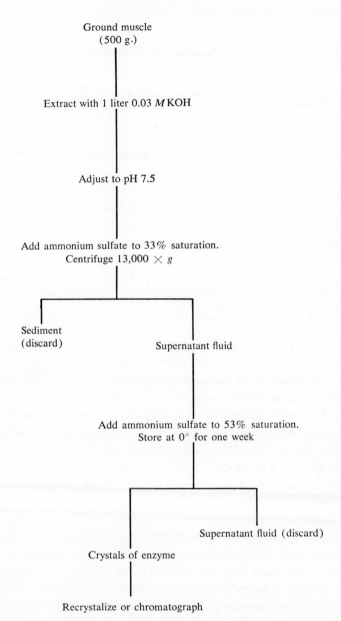

Figure 5–2. *Outline of an enzyme purification procedure. The enzyme used in this example is aldolase (see below in this chapter) and is uncommonly easy to crystallize. All operations are carried out in a cold room, from 0° to 5°.*

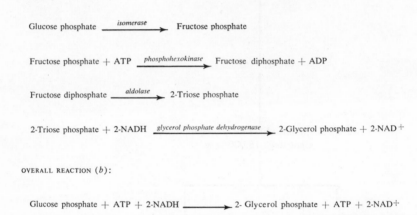

(a) Add excess glucose and the enzyme, hexokinase:

$$ATP + Glucose \xrightarrow{\textit{hexokinase}} Glucose\ phosphate$$

(b) Precipitate the hexokinase and measure the glucose phosphate formed by means of the following reactions:

$$Glucose\ phosphate \xrightarrow{\textit{isomerase}} Fructose\ phosphate$$

$$Fructose\ phosphate + ATP \xrightarrow{\textit{phosphohexokinase}} Fructose\ diphosphate + ADP$$

$$Fructose\ diphosphate \xrightarrow{\textit{aldolase}} 2\text{-Triose phosphate}$$

$$2\text{-Triose phosphate} + 2\text{-NADH} \xrightarrow{\textit{glycerol phosphate dehydrogenase}} 2\text{-Glycerol phosphate} + 2\text{-NAD}^+$$

OVERALL REACTION (*b*):

$$Glucose\ phosphate + ATP + 2\text{-NADH} \longrightarrow 2\text{- Glycerol phosphate} + ATP + 2\text{-NAD}^+$$

Figure 5–3.   *The measurement of ATP by an enzymatic technique. The method consists in allowing the ATP to phosphorylate glucose to form glucose phosphate. In the presence of excess glucose, each ATP molecule will give rise to one of glucose phosphate. The hexokinase is then precipitated by adding trichloroacetic acid. Analysis of glucose phosphate is accomplished by the addition of the enzymes shown, as well as excess ATP and NADH. Oxidation of NADH to NAD⁺ is followed with a spectrophotometer at 340 mμ, where NADH (but not NAD⁺) absorbs strongly. Note that for every molecule of glucose phosphate, two of NADH are oxidized.*

enzyme hexokinase, which phosphorylates the glucose to form glucose phosphate, after which the reaction is terminated by precipitating the hexokinase with acid. Then a mixture of the enzymes shown in the figure in parentheses is added to allow the stepwise conversion of glucose phosphate to two molecules of triose phosphate, which then oxidizes the coenzyme NADH to form NAD⁺. The significance of these reactions to the cell will be discovered later in the chapter. As stated earlier, NADH absorbs strongly at 340 mμ, whereas NAD⁺ does not. Thus each molecule of ATP ultimately leads to the oxidation of two molecules of NADH leading to a decline in absorbance at 340 mμ. The above represents a good example of the use of enzymes and enzyme systems as analytical reagents for the determination of their substrates, an approach which is of great value to the cell physiologist.

Cell metabolism: carbon sources and energy sources

Aerobic cells are generally able to break down sugars such as glucose in order to support life. It is easy to show that administration of radio-active (^{14}C) glucose to cells leads to a rapid labeling of a number of cell compounds; the inference is that glucose is serving as a source of cell carbon. Similarly, it may be shown that cells also use glucose as an energy source; that is, cells are able to couple thermodynamically un-favorable reactions to the degradation of glucose. Since one process appears to fulfill two necessities of the cell, it is very important to see how the two are related and to remember at all times that both are operative.

For example, it is known that administration of compounds which block energy transfer reactions prevent the incorporation of ^{14}C from glucose into cell material, indicating that mechanisms for carbon assimi-lation and energy conservation are closely interconnected. Other examples of the interconnection will be discussed later.

Utilization of glucose: glycolysis

Since it is impossible to give a complete description of the metabolic activities of the cell in a short space, we shall content ourselves with citing some pathways which both serve to illustrate important general aspects of metabolism and which are of central importance in them-selves. The assimilation of carbohydrates (such as the sugar—glucose) is a good case in point, as it not only leads to energy conservation in the cell, but also provides the starting point for the synthesis of a large number of cell components. We shall therefore adopt the tactic of imagining a cell floating in a medium (or in an intact organism), and we shall feed it some glucose and follow the process whereby it is taken up and used.

The first event is the obvious one of taking the glucose into the cell interior, where all subsequent reactions must take place. This is not necessarily a simple matter, as many cells possess permeability barriers to carbohydrates, and those that are able to admit them often do so by means of an energy-requiring "active transport" mechanism. Since such matters are discussed in detail in Chapter 8 we content ourselves here with pointing out that the barrier is likely to exist and that the uptake of the molecule, itself an energy source, may well require the expenditure of energy.

In understanding the subsequent chemical transformations of the glucose molecule, it is helpful to examine the structure of the molecule itself (see below). It has been known for a long time that glucose exists in solution largely as a six-membered-ring configuration. The reader should become familiar with both structures, as both are useful in visualizing the geometry of some of the reactions of interest. The reader is also reminded that, as a six-carbon sugar, glucose is one of a class of molecules called the *hexoses*, which, in turn, form a subclass of the monosaccharides.

After glucose has penetrated the cell interior, it is able to come into contact with the glycolytic enzymes found in the cytoplasm, apparently not associated with any organelle. The first reaction that takes place is the hexokinase-catalyzed phosphorylation of glucose to form glucose-6-phosphate, the phosphate coming from an adenosinetriphosphate (ATP) molecule. Since energy conservation through ATP synthesis will be seen to be one of the net results of glucose assimilation, we see a situation in the economy of the cell where a certain amount of energy must be expended to produce more, an occurrence reminiscent of "pump-priming" in economics.

Glucose-6-phosphate is then converted to its isomer, fructose-6-phosphate, which has a five-membered ring:

Glucose-6-phosphate*   Fructose-6-phosphate

The importance of the isomerization becomes clear at once when it is seen that the following reaction involves a second phosphorylation,

* We adopt the convention of writing the phosphate group as $\textcircled{P}$.

that of fructose-6-phosphate by ATP, to yield fructose 1,6-diphos-
phate:

Fructose-1,6-diphosphate

It is clear that the isomerization and subsequent phosphorylation have
left an essentially symmetrical molecule, with a phosphate projecting
from each end. Since one of the primary events in glycolysis is the
cleavage of a six-carbon sugar to form two similar three-carbon units,
the symmetry is of interest.

The cleavage, catalyzed by the enzyme aldolase, results in the formation of two similar, but not identical, triose phosphates, which are
themselves readily interconverted by an isomerase.

Thus the hexose unit has been twice phosphorylated and cleaved to yield
two identical triose phosphate molecules. Note that two molecules of
ATP are required to bring things to this state, not including a possible
requirement for ATP in connection with the transport of glucose into
the cell. Since ATP is in a real sense the energy currency of the cell, it is
plain that glycolysis must yield at least two molecules of ATP just to
break even.

In any case, since the two triose phosphate molecules are interconvertible, and since the cell has evolved a major pathway for the removal
of one of them, glyceraldehyde phosphate, we may consider it to

represent the important product of hexose diphosphate cleavage. In this instance the removal of a reaction product determines not only which of the triose phosphates is on the main stream of glycolysis, but even

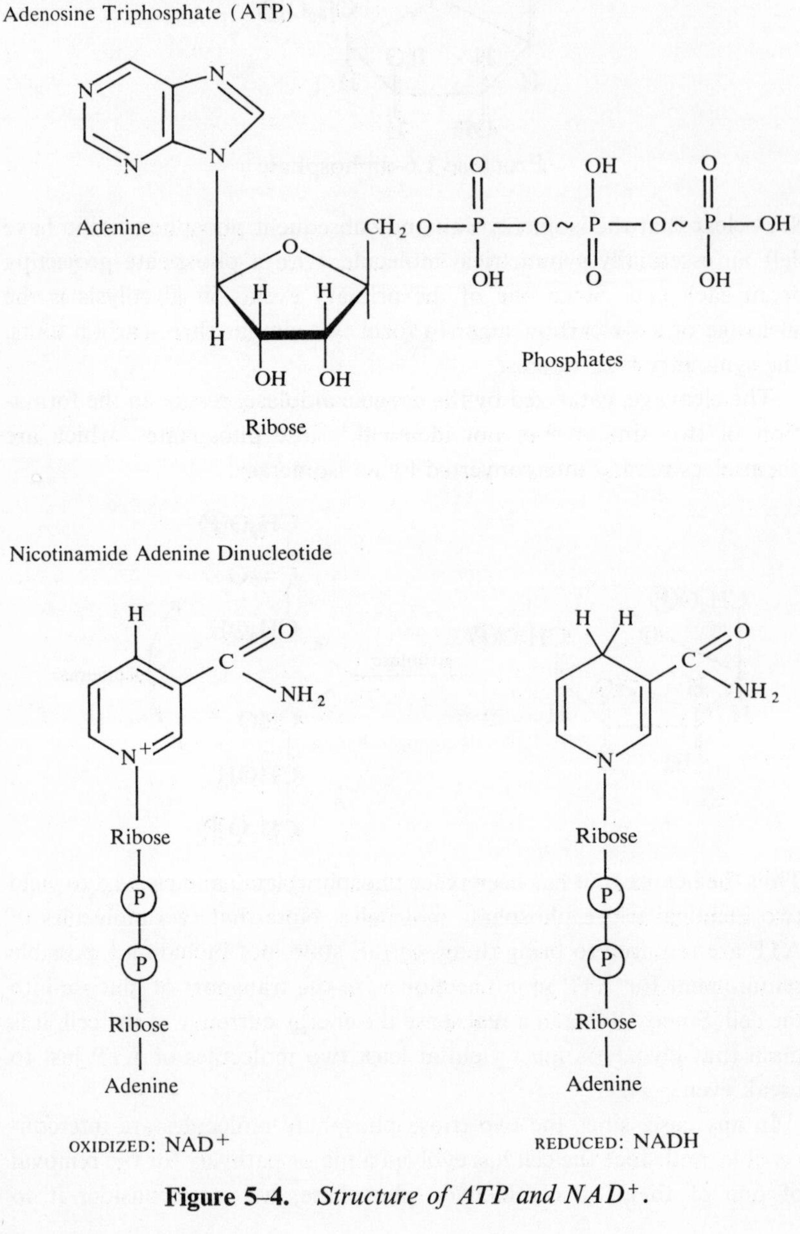
Adenosine Triphosphate (ATP)
Adenine
Ribose
Phosphates
Nicotinamide Adenine Dinucleotide
Ribose
Adenine
OXIDIZED: NAD+
REDUCED: NADH

Figure 5–4. *Structure of ATP and NAD*$^+$.

whether the main stream can move forward at all. It turns out that the equilibrium for the aldolase reaction is about 90 per cent in the direction of fructose diphosphate, so that if that reaction is not coupled to the removal of triose phosphate by subsequent enzymes, the pathway would not function. The fact that a major enzyme in an important pathway is found to have an equilibrium far in the opposite direction of its normal function illustrates the great importance of coupled reactions in metabolism. One might say that the aldolase reaction is thermodynamically unfavorable and therefore energy-requiring, and the energy is provided by coupling it to spontaneous reactions, in this case those involved in the removal of glyceraldehyde phosphate.

The next stage in glycolysis is the oxidation of glyceraldehyde phosphate. Oxidation is another way of saying that an electron is removed from the molecule, and, the world being what it is, if an electron is removed, it must be put somewhere. In this case the electron is transferred to a coenzyme molecule—specifically, a coenzyme that exists to transfer electrons from one molecule to another, nicotinamide adenine dinucleotide (NAD) (see Figure 5–4). NAD is reduced by picking up two electrons together with a hydrogen atom; it is then denoted NADH. Since there is a net positive charge on the oxidized molecule, we shall write it NAD^+. NAD^+ participates in a good number of cell reactions as an electron donor or acceptor (as a reducing or an oxidizing agent). We call it a *coenzyme* instead of a substrate for historical reasons and because it reacts with a number of different enzymes and might be said to assist them in their role of passing electrons about. In addition, NAD^+ exists in equilibrium between two interconvertible forms within the cell (oxidized and reduced), also a characteristic of coenzymes and not of substrates. Glyceraldehyde phosphate is oxidized in the presence of inorganic phosphate and NAD^+ to give diphosphoglycerate*:

$$\text{Glyceraldehyde phosphate} + H_3PO_4 + NAD^+ \rightleftharpoons$$
$$\text{Diphosphoglycerate} + NADH + H^+$$

(see also Figure 5–5). In this case the equilibrium is far to the right (toward products), so that this reaction might be said to pull the previous one. In addition, certain other gains have been made in the matter of extracting energy during the breakdown of glucose, but they are not

---

* The salt of diphosphoglyceric acid. Since biochemical chemical reactions take place around neutral pH, the salts are the major species and we shall denote them this way throughout.

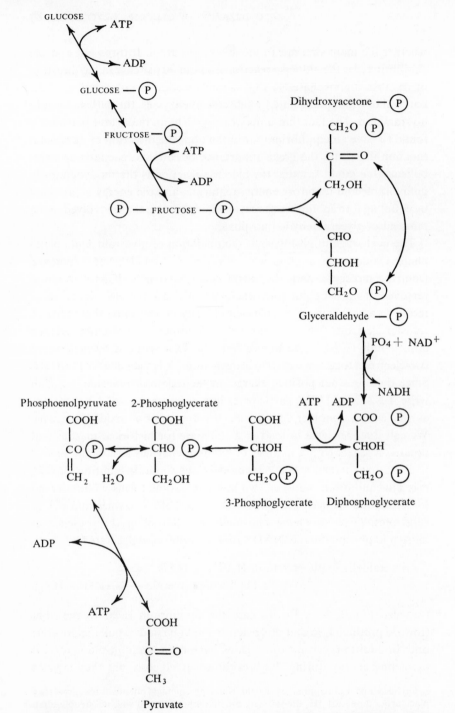

Figure 5–5. *Outline of glycolysis: the production of pyruvate from glucose.*

obvious without consideration of the structure of diphosphoglyceric acid. The reader has already noted that compounds involved in energy matters often have phosphate groups, as in ATP. A *high-energy compound* is generally one that is able to come apart very spontaneously, but in such a fashion as to allow coupling to other energy-requiring reactions. Hydrolysis of the terminal phosphate of ATP is a good case in point and will be seen in a number of contexts. Now, the fact is that all phosphorylated compounds are not necessarily "high-energy" compounds nor do all high-energy compounds contain phosphates, and it is worthwhile considering what constitutes a high-energy bond in a biological context. It will be recalled that a reaction (such as the hydrolysis of a bond) yielding energy is a spontaneous reaction, so a high-energy bond is generally one at which reactions occur readily. Most energy-yielding reactions in biology involve hydrolysis (the addition of water across a bond with subsequent cleavage). The energy-rich hydrolysis of the terminal phosphate of ATP is a good example. The spontaneity of cleavage of the last phosphate bond of ATP implies a large free energy change and the bond is often written as a wiggly line (see Figure 5–4). Indeed, other high-energy bonds of the cell have a somewhat similar configuration around them and in many cases may be written

$$
\begin{array}{ccc}
Y & & OH \\
\| & & | \\
-X & -O-P & -OH \\
& & | \\
& & O^-
\end{array}
$$

where Y represents carbon or oxygen and X is either carbon or phosphorus. In other words, a phosphate group attached to an atom which also bears a double bond may often be thought of as a high-energy phosphate compound and commonly written

$$
\begin{array}{c}
Y \\
\| \\
-X \sim PO_4
\end{array}
$$

The relatively high free energy of hydrolysis of a $\sim$ bond is related to the electronic structure of the molecule. For example, an important (but not total) reason for the high-energy character of the terminal phosphate bond of ATP is the fact that, at neutral pH, hydrolysis of the bond yields two negatively charged species, phosphate$^-$ and ADP$^-$. Since these similarly charged molecules tend to repel each other, the back reaction is minimized, and equilibrium is rather far in the direction of the products. A similar argument may be made for the other $\sim$ bonds, since the excess electrons on X due to the double bond impart a relative negative charge, which again tends to repel the phosphate group.

In any case, ATP conforms to this general structure with phosphorus X and oxygen as Y. Diphosphoglycerate has a similar structure,

$$
\begin{array}{ccc}
\text{O} & & \text{O}^- \\
\parallel & & | \\
\text{C}\!-\!\!-\text{O}\!-\!\!-\text{P}\!-\!\!-\text{OH} \\
| & & | \\
\text{H}\!-\!\text{C}\!-\!\text{OH} & & \text{O}^- \\
| \\
\text{CH}_2\text{O}\textcircled{P}
\end{array}
$$

this time with carbon as the X atom and oxygen as Y. Thus the reactions of glycolysis thus far should be regarded as a means of forming the characteristic high-energy phosphate arrangement. Once this is accomplished, all that remains is the transfer of the phosphate group from the high-energy "end" of diphosphoglyceric acid to adenosine diphosphate (ADP),

$$
\begin{array}{ccccc}
\text{COOP} & & & \text{COOH} \\
| & & & | \\
\text{HCOH} & +\ \text{ADP} \underset{\longleftarrow}{\overset{\text{transphosphorylase}}{\rightleftharpoons}} & \text{HCOH} & +\ \text{ATP} \\
| & & & | \\
\text{CH}_2\text{OP} & & & \text{CH}_2\text{OP}
\end{array}
$$

leading to the synthesis of two molecules of ATP for each one of glucose originally taken up.

Having made some ATP, the glycolytic pathway next involves structural rearrangements, preparatory to achieving the high-energy configuration again to make some more. First, phosphate is transferred from the 3 to the 2 position of glycerate:

$$
\begin{array}{ccc}
\text{COOH} & & \text{COOH} \\
| & & | \\
\text{H}\!-\!\text{C}\!-\!\text{OH} & \rightleftharpoons & \text{H}\!-\!\text{C}\!-\!\text{O}\textcircled{P} \\
| & & | \\
\text{CH}_2\text{O}\textcircled{P} & & \text{CH}_2\text{OH}
\end{array}
$$

Then, the enzyme enolase, which requires magnesium for activity, catalyzes a dehydration, thereby inserting a double bond in the molecule:

$$
\begin{array}{ccc}
\text{COOH} & & \text{COOH} \\
| & & | \\
\text{H—C—O}\textcircled{P} & \rightleftharpoons & \text{C—O—}\textcircled{P} + \text{H}_2\text{O} \\
| & & || \\
\text{CH}_2\text{OH} & & \text{CH}_2
\end{array}
$$

The resulting compound, phosphoenol pyruvate, is seen to exhibit the now familiar high-energy configuration with a double bond adjacent to a phosphate group. It is again possible to transfer phosphate from an energetic configuration in the phosphoenol pyruvate molecule to one at the terminal phosphate of ATP:

$$
\begin{array}{ccc}
\text{COOH} & & \text{COOH} \\
| & & | \\
\text{C—O—}\textcircled{P} & \longleftrightarrow & \text{C}=\text{O} \\
|| & & | \\
\text{CH}_2 & \text{ADP} \quad \text{ATP} & \text{CH}_3
\end{array}
$$

Four molecules of ATP have now been formed for every one of glucose utilized.

The other product of the reaction, pyruvate, is one of those pivotal compounds that lead in a number of directions, of which three are summarized in Figure 5–6. Note that pyruvate is reduced in the cases of lactate and ethanol formation. Note also that the reducing agent is NADH. It will be recalled that NADH was formed earlier in the pathway in connection with glyceraldehyde phosphate oxidation. The effect of these later reactions leading to NADH oxidation is to regenerate NAD$^+$, which can react again with glyceraldehyde phosphate to keep things going. This cyclic character in the role of NAD$^+$ in glycolysis is summarized in Figure 5–7. Neither the reactions leading to ethanol or lactate are of importance in aerobic cells, and we shall consider only the one major route, decarboxylation and fusion of the two carbon units to a coenzyme A residue to form acetyl-S—CoA. Coenzyme A, which bears one of the less informative names in biological chemistry, is a complex molecule,

$$
\begin{array}{c}
\textcircled{P} \qquad\qquad\qquad\qquad \text{CH}_3 \\
| \qquad\qquad\qquad\qquad\quad | \\
\text{Adenine—ribose—}\textcircled{P}\text{—}\textcircled{P}\text{—CH}_2\text{—C—CHOHCO—NHCH}_2\text{CH}_2\text{CO—} \\
| \\
\text{CH}_3 \qquad\qquad\qquad\qquad \text{—NHCH}_2\text{CH}_2\text{—SH}
\end{array}
$$

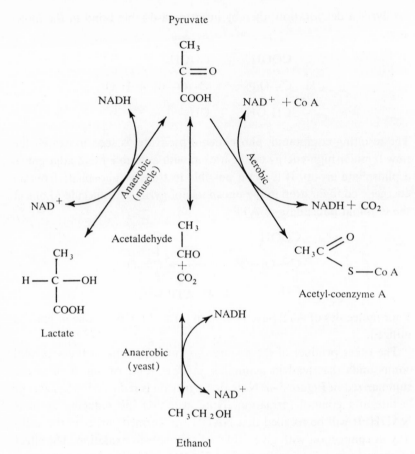

Figure 5–6. *Reactions of pyruvate. Note that aerobic metabolism of pyruvate leads to the formation of NADH, while anaerobic degradation leads to that of NAD⁺.*

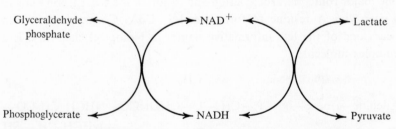

Figure 5–7. *The cyclic role of NAD⁺ in anaerobic metabolism.*

of which the business end is a sulfhydryl group. For this reason, we write it CoA—SH, to provide at least a little information about its functional nature. It is a molecule which appears again and again in cell physiology, largely in connection with fat metabolism, and so represents another branch point in the breakdown of glucose.

The precise mechanism of the oxidative decarboxylation of pyruvic acid is somewhat more complex than as described in Figure 5–6. The process may be broken down into several steps, the first being the decarboxylation itself. The reaction requires the presence of a phosphate compound of thiamine (vitamin B_1),

which turns out to be required for a number of other decarboxylations as well. This is a good example of the importance of vitamins as important cofactors in essential reactions of the cell, an observation which we shall make again in other contexts. The reaction also involves a second cofactor, a derivative of lipoic acid, which is likewise associated with decarboxylations of other compounds.

Energy yield of glycolysis

It is clear from the preceding discussion that an important result of the glycolytic breakdown of sugars is the synthesis of ATP and that a certain amount of ATP is used in the process. Thus we find a total of four moles of ATP synthesized per mole of glucose broken down, two each by phosphate transfer from diphosphoglycerate and phosphoenol pyruvate. On the other hand, the initial steps of glycolysis require the use of two molecules of ATP, which serve as phosphate donors. In other words, there is a net synthesis of two moles of ATP per glucose molecule. This represents the yield of that part of glucose breakdown that can occur in the absence of oxygen. We shall see in Chapter 6 that aerobic processes involved in the further degradation of pyruvate to CO_2 and H_2O can lead to much greater energy yields (see Table 6–1).

Of course, glucose is by no means the only carbohydrate used by cells, and energy yields depend on the exact situation. For example, glycogen, an extremely large and highly branched polymer of glucose, is an important carbohydrate storage form in many animal cells. The breakdown of glycogen requires inorganic phosphate and leads to the production of glucose phosphate without a requirement for ATP. For this reason, the formation of fructose diphosphate requires one, rather than two, molecules of ATP, and the net yield of ATP from glycogen is three, rather than two, as in the case of glucose.

The Krebs cycle

Further breakdown of glucose beyond acetyl-S—CoA requires the presence of oxygen and, from an energetic point of view, is by far the most important route for glucose metabolism. The first clues as to the mechanism by which it takes place were obtained prior to 1940, when it was learned that oxidation of pyruvate was stimulated by several dicarboxylic acids, of which one example was malic acid:

$$
\begin{array}{c}
\text{COOH} \\
|\\
\text{CHOH} \\
|\\
\text{CH}_2 \\
|\\
\text{COOH}
\end{array}
$$

It developed that oxidation of acetyl—S—CoA proceeds by a pathway involving four-carbon acids and which is commonly named after Krebs, who first described its cyclic nature.

One might say that the "primary" event of the Krebs (or citric acid) cycle is the fusion of a molecule of acetyl-S—CoA to a four-carbon diacarboxylic acid, oxaloacetate, to form citrate:

$$
\begin{array}{ccc}
& \text{COOH} & \text{CH}_2\text{COOH} \\
\overset{O}{\underset{\diagdown}{\overset{\diagup}{CH_3{-}C}}} + \overset{|}{\underset{|}{C{=}O}} & \rightleftharpoons & \text{HO}{-}\overset{|}{\underset{|}{CHCOOH}} + \text{CoA}{-}\text{SH} \\
\quad\;\; \text{S}{-}\text{CoA} \;\; \text{CH}_2 & & \text{CH}_2\text{COOH} \\
\qquad\qquad\quad \text{COOH} &
\end{array}
$$

The rest of the cycle is concerned with the conversion of citrate (six carbons) back to oxaloacetate (four) by a series of decarboxylations and

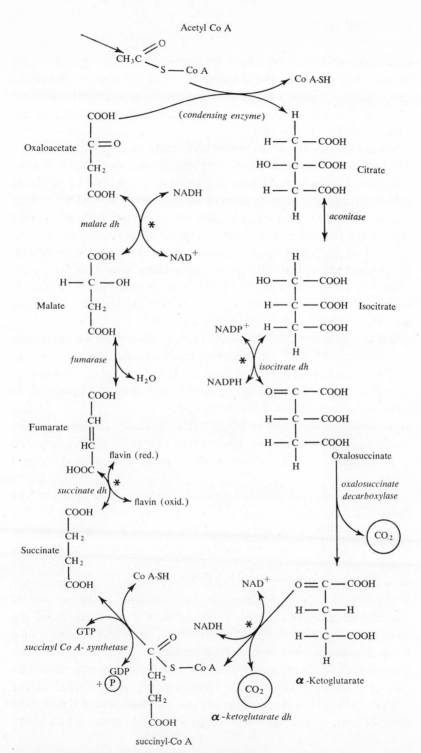

Figure 5–8. *The citric acid (Krebs) cycle. Names of enzymes are shown in italics. Dehydrogenase is abbreviated dh. Decarboxylations are emphasized by encircling the CO_2 produced. Oxidative steps are emphasized with an ∗.*

oxidations, which will be seen to be associated with energy conversion through ATP synthesis. The reactions by which this is accomplished are summarized in Figure 5–8 and represent a series of structural rearrangements leading to oxidations. For example, citrate is converted to isocitrate, which is then oxidized.

Some remarks about the individual reactions may be of interest. There are four oxidations in the cycle, of which two are linked to NAD^+ reduction. Of the others, isocitrate oxidation is catalyzed by isocitrate dehydrogenase and involves passage of an electron to $NADP^+$, which is similar to NAD^+, but with an additional phosphate in the ribose part (see above). Oxidation of succinate occurs by the passage of electrons to oxidized flavin bound to the enzyme which catalyzes the oxidation, succinic dehydrogenase. Obviously, mechanisms must exist for the re-oxidation of the NADH, NADPH, and reduced flavin molecules formed. The nature of these oxidations, which take place by way of the cytochrome chain, is the subject of Chapter 6.

It is also seen that there are two decarboxylations between citrate and oxaloacetate. Of these, the decarboxylation of α-ketoglutarate is very similar in mechanism to that of pyruvate, both leading to a coenzyme A derivative and both requiring a thiamine derivative and lipoamide as intermediates. Both are oxidative decarboxylations and the oxidizing agent (electron acceptor) is NAD^+. The similarity between the two reactions illustrates nature's tendency to operate with economy and to use similar techniques to accomplish similar ends wherever appropriate.

The reader will note that the purpose of the Krebs cycle, if it is only to degrade a six-carbon compound to one with four carbons, is fulfilled when succinyl-S—CoA is reached. The rest of the cycle might be looked on as only structural rearrangements leading to oxaloacetate, which would then pick up another acetyl-S—CoA molecule. This would be a serious mistake. It is a crude oversimplification to regard the Krebs cycle as only a mechanism for pyruvate removal. In fact, one of the chief functions of the cycle is to lead to ATP production, and the means whereby this is done will be described in detail later. For the time being, it is sufficient to note that ATP production is associated with each oxidative site of the cycle. More exactly, it is associated with the oxidation of NADH, NADPH, and reduced flavoprotein formed at the oxidative sites. Thus much of the organic chemistry of the Krebs cycle must be seen in the light of arrangements in structure which make oxidation possible; the nonoxidative steps prepare the way for the oxidative ones.

Although most of the ATP synthesis via the Krebs cycle, occurring by way of reoxidation of NADH or another electron donor, will be discussed in Chapter 6, there is one example of ATP production occurring in the cycle itself at the substrate level, so to speak. The formation of succinate from succinyl-S—CoA leads to one molecule of ATP by a two-step mechanism,

$$\text{Succinyl-S—CoA} + \text{GDP} + \text{phosphate} \rightleftharpoons \text{Succinate} + \text{GTP}$$

where GDP and GTP are guanosine di- and triphosphate, closely similar in structure to ADP and ATP. This is followed by a phosphate-group transfer reaction, leading to ATP synthesis:

$$\text{GTP} + \text{ADP} \rightleftharpoons \text{GDP} + \text{ATP}$$

It is interesting that the succinyl-S—CoA structure bears a strong resemblance to the high-energy configuration discussed earlier.

The role of the Krebs cycle in synthesis

A major function of the Krebs cycle is the coupling of hexose breakdown to a series of oxidations which lead to ATP formation. However, this is not the whole story, inasmuch as the cycle also plays an important role in the synthesis of a number of compounds required by the cell. We said that pyruvate and acetyl-S—CoA represent branch points in glycolysis, leading, in the case of acetyl-S—CoA, to the synthesis of fats and related compounds. Similarly, the Krebs cycle includes compounds which are important precursors, most notably in the synthesis of amino acids.

For example, α-ketoglutarate leads directly to the synthesis of the amino acid glutamate by the following reaction:

$$
\begin{array}{l}
\text{COOH} \\
| \\
\text{C}{=}\text{O} \\
| \\
\text{CH}_2 \\
| \\
\text{CH}_2 \\
| \\
\text{COOH}
\end{array}
\; + \text{NH}_3 + \text{NADH} \atop + \text{H}^+ \; \rightleftharpoons \;
\begin{array}{l}
\text{COOH} \\
| \\
\text{CHNH}_2 \\
| \\
\text{CH}_2 \\
| \\
\text{CH}_2 \\
| \\
\text{COOH}
\end{array}
\; + \text{NAD}^+ + \text{H}_2\text{O}
$$

Glutamate is, in turn, a precursor of a number of other amino acids, including ornithine, proline, and aspartate. The reaction

$$
\begin{array}{ccccc}
\text{COOH} & \text{COOH} & \text{COOH} & \text{COOH} \\
| & | & | & | \\
\text{CHNH}_2 & \text{C}{=}\text{O} & \text{C}{=}\text{O} & \text{CHNH}_2 \\
| & | & | & | \\
\text{CH}_2 & + & \text{CH}_2 & \rightleftharpoons & \text{CH}_2 & + & \text{CH}_2 \\
| & | & | & | \\
\text{CH}_2 & \text{COOH} & \text{CH}_2 & \text{COOH} \\
| & & | \\
\text{COOH} & & \text{COOH} \\
\text{Glutamate} & \text{Oxaloacetate} & \alpha\text{-Ketoglutarate} & \text{Aspartate}
\end{array}
$$

is an example of the class of reactions known as *transaminations*, which are very important in amino acid metabolism. Fumarate and succinyl-S—CoA both lead to a number of additional synthetic routes, so that Krebs cycle intermediates are constantly siphoned off at a number of locations to manufacture needed cell components. These interrelations of the Krebs cycle are summarized in Figure 5–9 and give a good idea of the central importance of the cycle in synthetic metabolism.

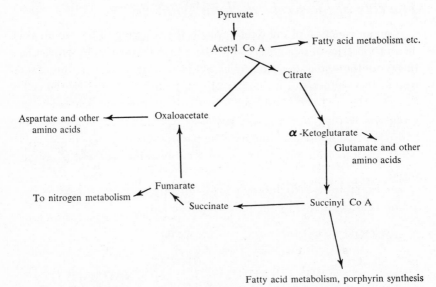

Figure 5–9. *Some side reactions of the Krebs cycle.*

The cycle is fundamentally involved in the energy-producing breakdown of hexose as well as many syntheses, most of which require energy.

This suggests that the traditional distinction between catabolic (breakdown) and anabolic (synthetic) pathways is quite invalid.

The glyoxylate cycle

The constant siphoning off of intermediates also raises a problem. The continued oxidation of acetyl-S—CoA by way of the cycle requires oxaloacetate to react with it. If there are no losses, each molecule of citrate will lead to one of oxaloacetate and the cycle will be truly catalytic. However, measurements using labeled acetate indicate that in bacteria most of the label is lost in one passage through the cycle—that most of the citrate leads to the synthesis of compounds other than oxaloacetate. This poses a serious problem, since if no mechanisms exist for the formation of additional oxaloacetate, the whole affair will grind to a halt.

Luckily for us, there are other routes for its synthesis. For example, in many cells an enzyme, called the *malic enzyme*, catalyzes the formation of malate from pyruvate by the reaction

$$\text{Pyruvate} + CO_2 + \text{NADPH} + H^+ \rightleftharpoons \text{Malate} + NADP^+$$

Note that the NADPH may be formed at the isocitric dehydrogenase step of the Krebs cycle, and that malate can be readily transformed to oxaloacetate by the malic dehydrogenase reaction

$$\text{Malic acid} + NAD^+ \rightleftharpoons \text{Oxaloacetic acid} + \text{NADH} + H^+$$

An additional system for replenishing Krebs cycle intermediates exists in many plant and bacterial cells (Figure 5–10) and is known as the *glyoxylate cycle*. It represents a sort of short circuit of the Krebs cycle, providing a way for additional acetyl-S—CoA to add carbon to the cycle intermediates. By it, each molecule of isocitrate leads to the formation of two four-carbon acids, succinate and malate, assisting in the maintenance of the level of oxaloacetate.

In addition, since the conversion of isocitrate to oxaloacetate is able to proceed by way of two different routes, a question of traffic control arises. The route involving the glyoxylate cycle is able to raise the concentrations of Krebs cycle intermediates, but at the expense of bypassing sites of energy trapping found in the intact Krebs cycle (see Chapter 6). The cell is placed in the position of determining and maintaining a

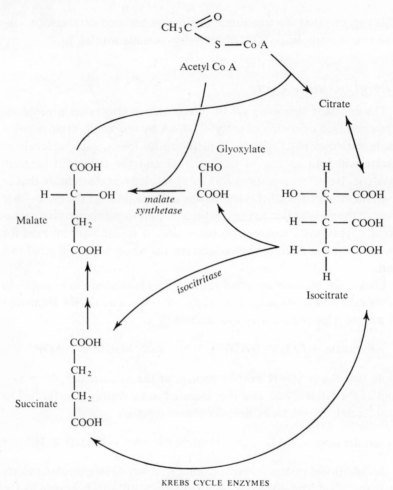

KREBS CYCLE ENZYMES

Figure 5–10. *The glyoxylate cycle. The names of the two enzymes of the cycle are given in italics.*

balance between energy trapping (in the form of ATP synthesis) and preserving optimal concentrations of the four-carbon acids, and the means whereby this is accomplished is instructive.

It will be recalled from Chapter 2 that effective feedback control mechanisms require a means of sensing output. In terms of metabolism, the question is simply which of the products of a given route are crucial in regulating the route. It will be seen below that oxaloacetate plays a significant role in regulation, and it should be clear that oxaloacetate would make a very sensitive indicator for the output of the glyoxylate cycle insofar as the maintenance of that level is the central role of the cycle. In fact, the actual control appears not to reside with oxaloacetate directly, but rather with a compound which is metabolically very close to it. Oxaloacetate may be synthesized from phosphoenol pyruvate by the following reversible reaction:

$$\text{Phosphoenol pyruvate} + CO_2 + IDP \rightleftharpoons \text{Oxaloacetate} + ITP$$

where IDP and ITP are inosine diphosphate and inosine triphosphate, both interconvertible with ADP and ATP. Thus buildup of oxaloacetate (when ATP is available) will support an increase in phosphoenol pyruvate (PEP). PEP is able to repress the synthesis of isocitritase, the first enzyme of the glyoxylate cycle, so that the feedback shown in Figure 5–11 occurs.

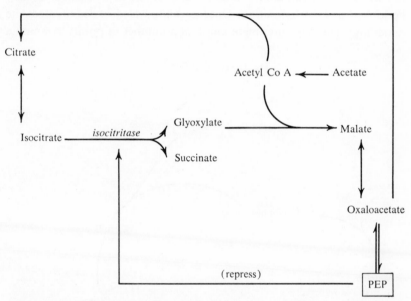

Figure 5–11. *Control of the glyoxylate cycle by phosphoenolpyruvate (PEP). Excess oxaloacetate leads to an increase in the concentration of PEP and repression of isocitritase formation, thus maintaining a steady level of oxaloacetate.*

The repression of an enzyme of the glyoxylate cycle by PEP leads to an additional aspect of the control, the stimulation of synthesis of this enzyme by acetate. Acetate is converted to acetyl-S—CoA, which is a precursor of the glyoxylate cycle and also has the effect of lowering the concentration of oxaloacetate by reacting with it to form citrate (Figure 5–6). Owing to the removal of oxaloacetate, the concentration of PEP becomes lower, and the repression of the glyoxylate cycle is lifted. This is a good example of a single regulatory mechanism that gives rise to either inductive and repressive effects, depending on the state of the cell.

Relationship between the Krebs cycle and nitrogen excretion

A final example of the close connections between the citric acid cycle and other metabolic processes is the manner in which the waste products of amino acid breakdown are eliminated. This is largely a problem of what to do with ammonia, since much of amino acid degradation may be looked at as deamination. Once an amino acid is deaminated, the remaining acid may enter metabolism at a number of points. Ammonia

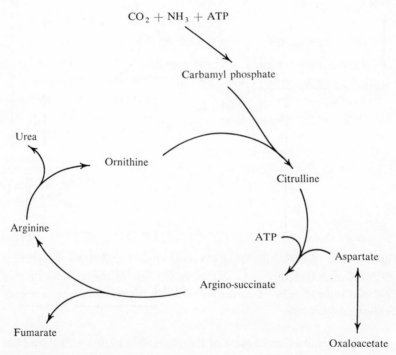

Figure 5–12. *Outline of pathway for urea formation. Note relation to the Krebs cycle via oxaloacetate and fumarate.*

is a relatively troublesome waste product, being rather caustic in solution (as NH_4OH). Aquatic vertebrates in many cases are able to wash away the ammonia into their environment rapidly enough to get by, but cells from other animals have found it more advantageous to eliminate nitrogen in the form of urea,

$$NH_2$$
$$|$$
$$C{=}O$$
$$|$$
$$NH_2$$

which has the advantage of including two waste products, NH_3 and CO_2 (for example, from the Krebs cycle). A brief examination of the pathway by which urea is made from ammonia (Figure 5–12) will show interrelations with the Krebs cycle (at fumarate and oxaloacetate) and again illustrates the cycle's central role in the chemical activities of the cell.

Control points of glycolysis and the Krebs cycle

We have made it clear that the glycolytic and Krebs pathways play a role in the cell involving much more than hexose metabolism, forming a sort of main line from which routes to many other syntheses branch off. Thus it would be hard to imagine a set of reactions more important to the living cell, and it is inconceivable that they should operate free of tight and sensitive controls. Regulation of these systems should include the possibility of shunting the breakdown of hexose to whatever synthesis is most relevant to the cell at the time and should also provide for adequate synthesis of ATP under whatever conditions prevail in the cell environment.

The most simple control of reactions in any metabolic sequence has to do with the direction in which the pathway may operate. Although all reactions may in principle be reversible, in fact many are essentially unidirectional under the conditions actually present (see Figure 5–13). Under cellular conditions, for example, many reactions involving the evolution of CO_2 are in effect one way, as mechanisms exist in the cell the rapid dissipation of the CO_2 formed. Since there are several decarboxylations in the breakdown of carbohydrates, these reactions provide a sort of barrier preventing the pathway as a whole from

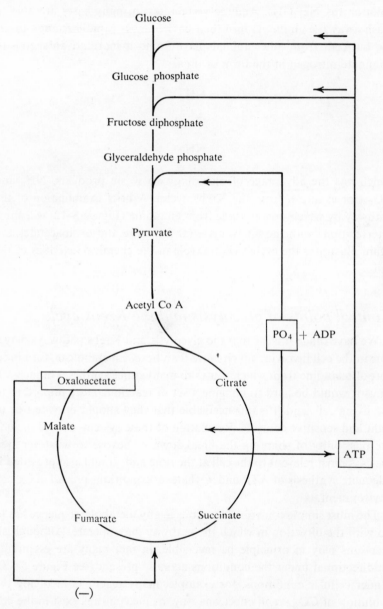

Figure 5–13. *Regulation of glycolysis and the Krebs cycle. Negative feedback by oxaloacetate, positive feedback by ATP, and competition for inorganic phosphate are illustrated. Details are given in the text.*

running backward. In fact, portions of the glycolytic (and Krebs) pathways will run in reverse, and such reversal is of extreme importance, to cite one example, in the light-induced synthesis of carbohydrates in green plants.

A number of comments may be made about the control of the glycolytic pathway. In the first place, control may be effected at the outset by the available hexose within the cell. The entry of hexose in many cases requires the presence of ATP. Thus it is possible to envision situations in which the available energy level of a cell might become so low that the path for additional ATP synthesis, glycolysis, and consequent relief from the energy depletion might be unavailable. A severe decline in ATP might thus be irreversible. It is likewise possible that the entry of hexose is under some sort of endocrine control in multicellular organisms. There is evidence that insulin affects the rate of hexose transport, providing an additional sort of control at the level of hexose entry.

Once in the cell, hexose must be phosphorylated (twice) using ATP. Since ATP itself is produced farther on in the pathway, this represents a form of positive feedback of "the more you have, the more you get" variety. But a system under the regulation of positive feedback only would be rather explosive. Luckily for us, the positive regulation by ATP is opposed by several important negative controls involving the pyridine nucleotides, NAD^+ and NADH, as well as in organic phosphate. NAD^+ plays an especially important role in coordinating the rates of flow through the different parts of the glycolytic pathway. This is because NAD^+ is required at a fairly early stage in glycolysis for the triose phosphate dehydrogenase reaction, leading to NADH formation. The NADH thus formed is required for the reduction of pyruvate farther along, to form ethanol or lactate. Under anaerobic conditions, where the oxidation of NADH by molecular oxygen does not take place, the linkage between NADH formation and utilization is quite tight and apparent significance in keeping the two ends of glycolysis going at rates consistent with each other.

The presence of oxygen leads to a different situation. In the first place, the oxidations of the Krebs cycle, all of which require molecular oxygen, can now take place. For example, NADH oxidation proceeds rapidly by an aerobic mechanism described in Chapter 6. Thus the "addition" of oxygen leads to more NAD^+ and less NADH, which would have the effect of preventing the synthesis of lactate from pyruvate (which requires NADH) and favoring the synthesis of acetyl-S—CoA (which requires NAD$^+$), which then leads to the Krebs cycle.

The Pasteur effect

An oxygen-induced increase in the NAD$^+$/NADH ratio might lead one to expect stimulation of glycolysis as a whole, owing to an increase in the rate of the triose phosphate dehydrogenase step. Although a reasonable expectation, it is quite untrue. It was discovered about a century ago by Pasteur that oxygen inhibits glycolysis, measured as the rate of carbohydrate breakdown. In other words, it is clear that some-thing other than the NAD$^+$ oxidation-reduction state is regulating the rate of glycolysis in the presence of oxygen.

This inhibition of glycolysis, which is called the *Pasteur effect*, probably involves a complex mechanism, but it is becoming increasingly clear that an important part of the control resides in the availability of phosphate for the various reactions that require it. Glycolysis requires inorganic phosphate at the level of glyceraldehyde phosphate dehydro-genase, and in its absence the whole pathway must come to a halt. Phosphate is also required in the various oxidations of the Krebs cycle, and, for reasons discussed in Chapter 6, about three molecules of phos-phate are required at each of the four oxidations for the cycle to operate at full rate. This means that, in the presence of oxygen, the Krebs cycle will compete very effectively with glycolysis, and the low availability under aerobic conditions might account in large measure for inhibition of glycolysis, primarily at the glyceraldehyde phosphate dehydrogenase step. It should be added that, because glycolysis is largely cytoplasmic, while Krebs cycle enzymes are located in the mitochondrion, the com-petition for phosphate is also influenced by the ability of the mitochon-drial membrane to effect its transport.

The role of the oxaloacetate in regulation

There are also feedback controls operating in the Krebs cycle to maintain its rate between limits. Obviously, oxaloacetate is required at the outset of the cycle to lead to the formation of citrate, so that any process limiting the concentration of oxaloacetate could limit the rate of the whole cycle. Oxaloacetate has, however, an additional controlling effect, as it is known to inhibit some of the reactions leading to its own production. For example, oxaloacetate is known to be a potent competitive inhibitor of succinate dehydrogenase, so that excessive increase in its concentration would lead to inhibition of its formation until a lower level was attained. Oxaloacetate is also an inhibitor of malate oxidation and appears to influence enough other mitochondrial reactions to suggest that it is a focal point of control in oxidative metabolism as a whole.

Constant proportions of enzymes

We have seen that the concentration of an enzyme in solution directly influences the rate of reaction and that enzyme concentrations are subject to control. Obviously other forms of regulation will be of little use if enzyme concentrations are either in enormous excess or are insufficient to carry on reactions at a rate commensurate with the rate of the pathway as a whole. In this connection, it is interesting that mitochondria isolated from different tissue contain groups of enzymes which exist in constant proportion to each other, no matter what the source. For example, the enzymes of pyruvate oxidation and the Krebs cycle form a constant pattern in different tissues, with the activity of malate dehydrogenase exceeding that of glutamate transaminase by a factor of about two. The transaminase in turn exceeds succinate dehydrogenase and pyruvate decarboxylase by a factor of about ten. These constant patterns suggest that there are mechanisms by which the production of enzymes is adjusted to levels required for their over-all function. The absence or presence of a constant proportion between two enzymes is also useful in determining whether or not the two enzymes are functionally related *in vivo*—whether their connection by a pathway represents an important route of interconversion in the real cellular world.

The preceding paragraphs have given examples of regulatory mechanisms in hexose metabolism, but the examples are by no means inclusive. Additional ones will appear in Chapter 6, and for more detail the reader is directed to the book by Lehninger or the symposium edited by Tager et al., both listed in the Suggested Reading for this chapter. It is useful, however, to point out that there are three general sorts of regulation which together include the cases that we have examined. In the first place, feedback inhibition of enzyme activity plays an important role, as in oxaloacetate control of the Krebs cycle. A second order of control of the pathways involves regulation of enzyme synthesis, so that enzymes are present in appropriate concentrations to their role. A good example is repression of the glyoxylate cycle by PEP. Finally, competition for common intermediates plays a central role in metabolic pathways. Important control points are defined by intermediates used in a number of different reactions and not present in too large excess. For example, acetyl-S—CoA probably plays such a part in that it is at once involved in fatty acid synthesis, the glyoxylate pathway, and the oxidation of pyruvate, so that the processes (among others) are in competition for it and essentially regulate each other by their ability to compete. Other common intermediates which appear to exert control on glycolysis and the Krebs cycle include NAD^+, phosphate, and, as we shall see, ADP. In many cases the regulation depends on a balance between two components, so that glycolysis is really under the control of the NADH/NAD^+ ratio and, for reasons that will shortly become clear, the Krebs cycle is sensitive to regulation by ADP/ATP.

Suggested Reading

CIBA Foundation Symposium, *Regulation of Cell Metabolism*, G. E. W. Wolstenholme and C. M. O'Connor (eds.), Little, Brown and Co., Boston, 1959.

Fruton, J. S., and S. Simmonds, *General Biochemistry*, John Wiley & Sons, New York, 2nd ed., 1958, Chap. 18–21.

Greenberg, D. M. (ed.), *Metabolic Pathways*, Vols. I and II, Academic Press, New York, 1960–1961.

Kornberg, H. L., and S. R. Elsden, "The metabolism of 2-carbon compounds by microorganisms," in *Advances in Enzymology*, F. F. Nord (ed.), Vol. 23, Interscience, New York, 1961.

Krebs, H. A., "The tricarboxylic acid cycle," in *The Harvey Lectures*, 1949–1950, Academic Press, New York, 1950.

Lehninger, A. L., *Bioenergetics*, W. A. Benjamin, New York, 1965.

Tager, J. M., S. Papa, E. Quagliariello, and E. C. Slater, *Regulation of Metabolic Processes in Mitochondria*, Elsevier, New York, 1966.

CHAPTER 6

Energy Conservation in Cells—Nonphotosynthetic

It was said in Chapter 5 that a central consequence of the aerobic breakdown of hexose is ATP synthesis, which occurs at the oxidative steps of the Krebs cycle. Since ATP is involved in most of the energy-requiring reactions of the cell, clearly its synthesis is of great importance in the life of the cell, and the control of its formation would be expected to play a role in the control of numerous other events. This being the case, it is worthwhile to examine the matter of ATP formation in more detail and to pay special attention to the matter of its control.

ATP is formed by the esterification of inorganic phosphate with the terminal phosphate of ADP:

Cells have evolved three main routes to ATP synthesis, including substrate-linked phosphorylation (as in glycolysis), photosynthetic phosphorylation (see Chapter 7), and oxidative phosphorylation, which is the subject of this chapter. In addition, there are a number of ways ATP may be formed without a net increase in the available energy, an example being the myokinase reaction:

$$2ADP \rightleftharpoons ATP + AMP*$$

Additional routes leading to ATP synthesis include a number of phosphate exchanges where phosphate is transferred from another nucleotide triphosphate (such as guanosine triphosphate) to ADP. Such reactions encountered earlier in the Krebs cycle do not result in an increase of "high-energy phosphate" but rather a change in its identity.

The reactions that lead to a net increase in high-energy phosphate compounds, of which ATP is the most important, have one central feature in common, and that feature will be stated here in the form of a *central dogma: Cells obtain energy only by moving electrons.* One can be a bit more explicit and say that cells really only capture energy by dropping electrons from a higher energy state to a lower one. A physiologist of a chemical persuasion would put it a bit differently, saying that energy transfer in cells is a matter of oxidation and reduction. It will be recalled that oxidation is the removal of an electron from something, while reduction is adding it on somewhere else. Obviously the two must be coupled together, because, when something is reduced, something else must be oxidized. The truth of the central dogma is seen in the fact that all respiratory ATP synthesis is coupled to oxidations and, specifically, to the transfer of electrons from a substrate such as a Krebs cycle acid, where they may be said to have a high energy, to an electron acceptor such as oxygen. The difference between the energy of the electron in the substrate and in oxygen represents the amount of energy available to make ATP.

Photosynthesis will be seen in Chapter 7 to involve the passage of electrons from a high-energy state of the chlorophyll molecule to another acceptor, coupled to the synthesis of ATP. The applicability of the central dogma to the substrate-linked synthesis of ATP coupled to anaerobic glycolysis (see Chapter 5) is a bit more subtle. Suffice it to say that, in the breakdown of hexose, ATP formation is coupled to the

*AMP = adenosine monophosphate.

passage of electrons from one part of the glycolytic pathway to another, carried in the form of NADH. Indeed, glycolysis is an example of the more general class of pathways called *fermentation*, which we define as a system for coupling ATP synthesis to electron flow where the electron donor is an organic compound and the acceptor is a second organic compound derived from the first:

$$\text{Hexose} \longrightarrow \text{Triose-}\textcircled{P} \longrightarrow \text{Pyruvate} \longrightarrow \text{Lactate (or EtOH)}$$

$$\text{NADH}$$

It is easy to observe that cellular energy capture invariably involves the movement of electrons, but the nature of the coupling between electron flow and ATP synthesis is a subject of intense research and remains, except in the case of substrate-linked phosphorylation, largely un-explained. The coupling process, which might be summarized

$$\begin{array}{c} \textbf{ADP} \\ +\textcircled{P}\ \textbf{ATP} \end{array}$$

$$\textbf{Electron donor} \longleftrightarrow \textbf{Acceptor}$$

is unclear, both in general outline and in particulars. In fact, recent experimental work has been quite unable to distinguish between two widely differing theories of the coupling process, an impasse which is discussed below.

There is, however, a great deal of knowledge about the mechanisms for oxidation itself, and a large body of descriptive information exists about ATP synthesis, although the mechanism is, as we said, unclear. Much of what is known about the process is directly related to the matter of control of ATP production and is discussed below.

Oxidation-reduction enzymes

There are a huge number of known oxidative enzymes, and their study is a field of its own, with special techniques and language. For our purposes, we will consider all the enzymes as falling into one of two classes and consider the properties of the classes as a whole.

1. One class includes enzymes that catalyze oxidations by accepting electrons themselves and thus altering their own oxidation-reduction state.

2. Another class includes only enzymes that mediate the transfer of electrons between donor and acceptor without serving as electron donor or acceptor.

An example of the first sort of enzyme is succinic dehydrogenase, which catalyzes the oxidation of succinate by withdrawing two electrons, which reduce the flavin prosthetic group of the enzyme itself. The enzyme is then oxidized by another enzyme and is again ready to accept electrons from succinate. In a very real sense such an enzyme is both a catalyst and a reactant.

A good example of the second class of enzymes is malate dehydrogenase, which catalyzes the oxidation of malate by NAD^+. The enzyme, in this case, is not oxidized or reduced and might be said to have the function of bringing malate and the pyridine nucleotide, NAD^+, together in the right spatial arrangement to ensure rapid reaction. Both of these enzymes are called *dehydrogenases*, as both react with a substrate in an oxidation involving removal of two hydrogens. The central event in the oxidation involves the removal of electrons, rather than hydrogen, and it is probably fair to say that these oxidations involve the transfer of hydrogen only in a secondary sense, after electron transfer has taken place. This statement is based on the fact that the subsequent oxidation of succinate dehydrogenase or NAD^+ occurs by way of steps where only electron transfer appears to take place. The two processes are, however, very hard to separate, since hydrogen ion is involved in a fundamental way with ATP synthesis itself.

A general equation for oxidative enzyme action is given as

$$AH_2 + B \rightleftharpoons BH_2 + A$$

or

$$A \text{ (reduced)} + B \text{ (oxidized)} \rightleftharpoons A \text{ (oxidized)} + B \text{ (reduced)}$$

In our first class of enzymes, B is a part of the enzyme itself, whereas in the second it is a separate entity, often called a *coenzyme*, as in the case of NAD^+.

The respiratory chain

Let us turn our attention now to the specific oxidations involved in the Krebs cycle. They are listed in Table 6–1, which also includes information about the quantity of ATP synthesized per mole of reactant. In the table it is seen that one of the four oxidations is linked to the reduction of the enzyme itself, while the others have one or the other of the

TABLE 6–1

OXIDATIONS OF THE KREBS CYCLE

Reaction	Electron Acceptor	Moles of ATP
Isocitrate dehydrogenase	$NADP^+$	3
α-Ketoglutarate dehydrogenase	NAD^+	4
Succinate dehydrogenase	the enzyme (flavin group)	2
Malate dehydrogenase	NAD^+	3

pyridine nucleotides as acceptor. It is worth adding at this point that the reason for the four ATP's produced at the α-ketoglutarate dehydrogenase step is due to an extra substrate-linked phosphorylation similar to those described in Chapter 5. For our purposes it is also worth noting that enzymes termed *transhydrogenases* catalyze the conversion of NADH to NADPH and vice versa, so that we may regard the two as largely equivalent, as far as the table is concerned.

The only remaining questions about the reactions listed in the table concern the reoxidation of either the enzyme, in the case of succinate dehydrogenase, or NADH in the others. The mechanism of such oxidations is known in considerable detail, and it must be said that the pathways for such electron transfer are surprisingly complex, even without considering the still more complex matter of how ATP is formed in the process. In animal or plant mitochondria the ultimate electron acceptor is molecular oxygen, while in bacteria it can be oxygen or an inorganic oxidant such as nitrate, sulfate, or oxidized iron. In the case of mitochondrial oxidations, the oxygen is reduced to water, and the over-all process may be written

$$2AH_2 + O_2 \longrightarrow 2A + 2H_2O$$

The 2:1 ratio of substrate to oxygen is a reflection of the fact that oxidation of the substrate involves removal of two electrons, whereas reduction of one molecule of oxygen to give water involves four. There are some oxidations in the cell that give rise to hydrogen peroxide (H_2O_2), but the enzyme catalase, which is a universal cellular constituent, converts it to water and oxygen, rendering the equation above still valid. Obscured in the arrow of the equation is a chain of oxidation-reductions of some complexity. This involves a series of different enzymes, each of which accepts electrons from its predecessor and passes them on to the following carrier. For example, one of the carriers, cytochrome c, now oxidized, picks up another electron from the preceding cytochrome c_1, and so on. These electron transfers may be summarized by writing

$$\text{Cytochrome } c_1 \longrightarrow \text{Cytochrome } c \longrightarrow \text{Cytochrome } a$$

where the arrows denote, not conversion of c_1 to c, but the transfer of an electron from one to the other. The complete system for aerobic electron transfer, which is known as the *respiratory chain*, is shown in Figure 6–1.

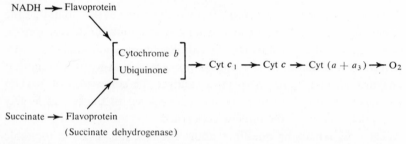

Figure 6–1. *The path of electrons in the respiratory chain. The order of involvement of cytochrome* b *and ubiquinone is not well understood, but the two appear to be closely associated.*

It is seen to have two branches at the substrate end, one involved in NADH oxidation and the other in succinate oxidation. Some of the carriers are listed in Table 6–2, and it is seen that they include enzymes, either flavin- or heme-containing, as well as small molecules. The reader will remember (from Chapter 2) that there is a relationship between the standard potential of a reaction and the free energy change. It is quite literally true that the carriers of the respiratory chain are arranged in order of decreasing energy, which is expressed in Table 6–2 as an increasing potential. An electron from succinate, as it passes to oxygen via the chain, passes down an energy gradient which is reflected in the difference in potential between succinate and oxygen. This energy difference is available for ATP synthesis.

TABLE 6–2

ELECTRON CARRIERS OF THE RESPIRATORY CHAIN

Carrier	Protein?	Prosthetic Group	Number of Electrons Carried	E_0
NAD$^+$	no	—	2	-0.31
Flavoprotein	+	flavin	2	-0.05
Succinate	no	—	2	0.03
Cytochrome b	+	heme	1	0.06
Ubiquinone	no	—	2	0.09
Cytochrome c_1	+	heme	1	0.22
Cytochrome c	+	heme	1	0.26
Cytochrome a	+	heme	1	0.2
Oxygen	no	—	4	0.79

The exact nature of the oxidation-reduction carriers has been a subject for study over the last half century, and our knowledge is quite detailed. A number of different flavoproteins have been studied which have a phosphate derivative of riboflavin as their prosthetic group,

where R represents either phosphate, in the case of flavin mononucleotide (FMN) or AMP, in the case of flavin adenine dinucleotide (FAD). The oxidation or reduction of the flavoprotein takes place at the prosthetic group by a two-electron transition:

with the two electrons being transferred either together or sequentially.

Ubiquinone (also called coenzyme Q) is likewise oxidized by a two-electron transition and has the structure

$$CH_3O \begin{array}{c} O \\ \| \\ \end{array} CH_3 \left[CH_2 - CH = \underset{\underset{CH_3}{|}}{C} - CH_2 \right]_n H$$

where the side chain may be of variable length. The exact location of ubiquinone in the respiratory chain is not clear, and it has even been suggested that it is not on the main line of the chain, because it is not oxidized and reduced at a rate high enough to be consistent with the rate of flow of electrons through the chain. A special role for ubiquinone in ATP synthesis has been suggested, but the evidence is quite inconclusive.

The cytochromes are all heme proteins whose oxidation-reduction occurs at the iron atom within the heme ring system:

They are generally red, and each cytochrome exhibits a characteristic spectrum. Dramatic changes in the spectrum are produced when they are oxidized or reduced, so that it is comparatively easy to examine the different cytochromes in intact mitochondria and to determine their rates of reaction and oxidation-reduction state. It is fortunate that there are spectroscopic approaches to the study of cytochromes, since, with the exception of cytochrome c, all are found to be integral parts of the mitochondrial membrane systems and have not been obtained in pure form without considerable alteration. Cytochrome c, on the other hand, is extremely easy to isolate, being apparently soluble in the intramitochondrial space. Cytochrome c is one of the relatively few proteins whose complete amino acid sequence is known, and its enzymic action has been studied in impressive detail.

It should be pointed out here that the cytochromes are quite unusual enzymes in that they react directly with other enzymes rather than substrates of lower molecular weight. Their action is so much a matter of electron flow down the chain that ordinary enzyme kinetics are not always easy to apply, and sometimes hydrodynamic analogies seem more valid.

Since the respiratory chain appears to form an integral part of the mitochondrial structure (or, in the case of bacteria, of the cell membrane), it has been a challenging object of study. The construction of the chain and especially the manner of coupling of electron flow to ATP synthesis have become clear largely through the use of inhibitors (see

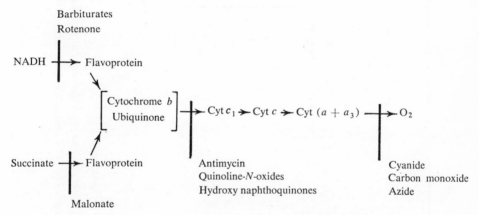

Figure 6–2. *Inhibitors of the respiratory chain.*

Figure 6–2). For example, the addition of an inhibitor such as antimycin in the presence of NADH has the effect of rendering cytochrome c_1 through a and a_3 more oxidized, while cytochrome b and flavoproteins are more reduced. By a number of such experiments, the order of the carriers in the chain has become known. The use of inhibitors, together with artificial electron acceptors (Figure 6–3), has led to the study of isolated portions of the chain and has greatly assisted in localizing the sites of ATP formation. For example, the oxidation of ascorbate in the presence of antimycin seems to give rise to one molecule of ATP, succinate oxidation yields two, and NADH, three.

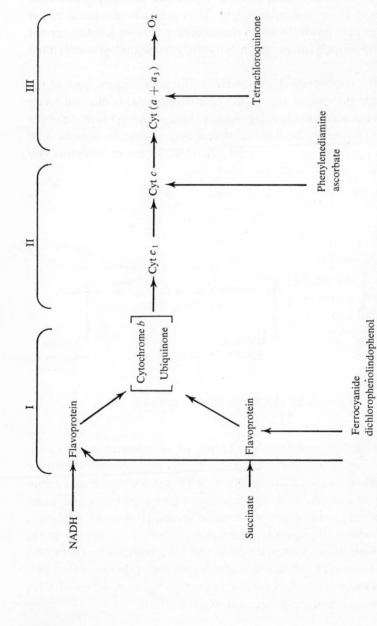

Figure 6-3. *The reaction of artificial electron carriers with the respiratory chain. Regions of ATP synthesis are indicated by Roman numerals. There does not appear to be ATP formation associated with the portion of the chain between succinate and the cytochrome b–ubiquinone locus.*

Oxidative ATP synthesis

As we said, the exact mechanism of coupling between oxidation and phosphorylation of ADP is not known. A large number of the opinions that exist about the subject have grown up through argument by analogy from substrate-linked phosphorylation or from studies using different inhibitors of the process. For example, there is a class of compounds, of which 2,4-dinitrophenol,

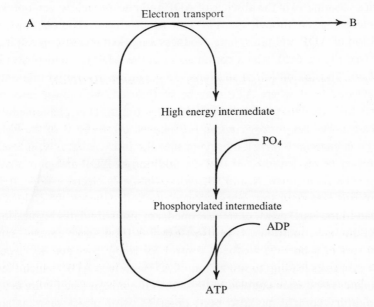

is the best known, that effectively uncouple oxidations from ATP formation. Addition of such compounds often stimulates electron flow

Figure 6–4. *Outline of a mechanism for ATP synthesis. The final stage is the transfer of phosphate from the phosphorylated high energy intermediate to ADP to form ATP. The chemical nature of the intermediate, as well as the coupling of its formation to electron transport, is unknown.*

while completely preventing any ATP synthesis. Studies of this kind have led to a picture of ATP synthesis, given in Figure 6–4, involving the synthesis of high-energy intermediates which lead to ATP. Although a large body of evidence supports this picture, the fact is that efforts to identify or isolate the intermediates have met with failure. The reason given is usually their extreme instability, but difficulty of isolation may also be a measure of the fact that they may not exist at all. Indeed, an alternative theory of ATP formation has been put forward in which high-energy intermediates in the sense of the figure *do not* exist, and this theory is discussed below in the more appropriate context of Chapter 8.

Respiratory control

Whatever the mechanism of the coupling process, there is one aspect of it with profound significance as far as the control of ATP production is concerned. If isolated mitochondria are incubated with a substrate (such as succinate) in the absence of ADP and phosphate, oxygen uptake is detected, even though no ATP can be produced. The subsequent addition of ADP and phosphate produces a marked increase in respiration (see Figure 6–5), which continues until the ADP (or phosphate) is used up. Thus oxidation of succinate occurs at the maximum rate only under conditions where ATP may be synthesized, with lower rates of "wasteful" oxidation of substrate at other times. This phenomenon, which is called *respiratory control*, is explained on the basis of the *high-energy intermediate theory* by saying that the intermediate, X, is itself inhibitory to respiration and that the addition of ADP and phosphate effects the removal of X and therefore stimulates electron flow. It is interesting that an uncoupling agent such as dinitrophenol, which is said to lead to the breakdown of the intermediate, also stimulates respiration under similar conditions. It is also clear that respiratory control may form sort of a positive feedback control for respiratory activity, since most processes leading to utilization of ATP produce ADP, which then stimulates respiration coupled to further ATP synthesis (see Figure 6–6). Respiratory control has also been observed with intact mammalian cells, which suggests that it is not simply a property of isolated mitochondria.

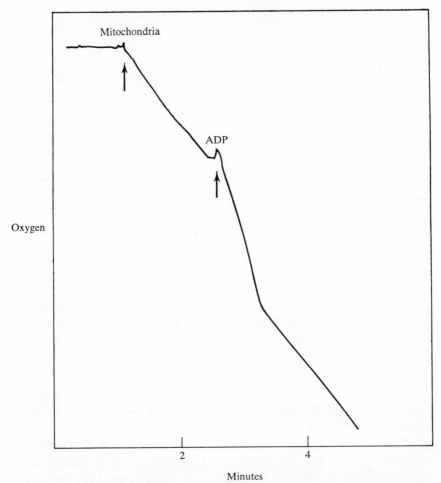

Figure 6–5. *Respiratory control: the stimulation of mitochondrial respiration by ADP. This is a trace produced by a polarographic electrode sensitive to oxygen. A downward deflection of the line indicates an increase in the rate at which oxygen is used up. The reaction mixture at the beginning of the experiment (left side of the chart) contains buffer, magnesium, phosphate, succinate, and water and is saturated with oxygen. When a suspension of mitochondria, obtained as described in Figure 1–6, is introduced, oxygen uptake occurs as succinate is oxidized to fumarate. The addition of ADP stimulates oxygen consumption, which returns to the original rate when the ADP has all been phosphorylated to form ATP. The amount of oxygen that is used at the higher rate may serve as the basis for estimating the efficiency of ATP synthesis—i.e., the ATP/oxygen ratio.*

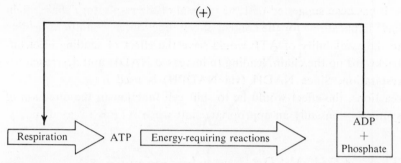

Figure 6–6. *Respiratory control. ATP utilization produces ADP and phosphate which, in turn, stimulate respiration.*

The reversibility of the respiratory chain

Recent evidence indicates that the reactions of the respiratory chain are reversible and that electrons may be made to flow in the direction of the substrate. Since the flow is up the energy gradient, the reaction requires energy, instead of leading to its production. For instance, electrons may be inserted into the chain at the cytochrome *c* locus and, in the presence of cyanide, pass back along the chain to reduce cytochromes *b*, ubiquinone, or even NAD^+. This reaction requires ATP and so seems to involve a reversal not only of the chain but of the energy-coupling reactions shown in Figure 6–4.

A similar reversal reaction may be demonstrated using succinate as the electron donor, which, in the presence of antimycin (which inhibits the respiratory chain between cytochromes *b* and *c*) and ATP, leads to NAD^+ reduction. This reaction,

$$\text{Succinate} + NAD^+ + ATP \longrightarrow$$
$$\text{Fumarate} + NADH + H^+ + ADP + PO_4$$

is also uphill, since it was seen in Table 6–2 that NAD^+ is of a higher energy than succinate. The reaction proceeds even in the absence of antimycin, under which condition ATP is not required, suggesting that high-energy intermediates are being formed in one part of the chain (between cytochrome *b* and oxygen) and are then used in the reduction of NAD^+. In fact, ADP inhibits the reduction, indicating that ATP synthesis is in competition with the reversal reaction for the intermediates themselves, a kind of experiment that lends some credence to the existence of intermediates, even if they are difficult to identify.

It has been suggested that the reversal of the respiratory chain might have implications for the control of cell function, as conditions leading to the availability of ATP would have the effect of sending electrons backward up the chain, leading to increased NADH and decreased net respiration. Since NADH (via NADPH) is used in many synthetic reactions, the effect would be to shift cell function in the direction of synthesis—possibly an appropriate shift when ATP is in good supply.

The NADH–NADPH transhydrogenase

A final point related to the matter of control of respiratory activity concerns the transhydrogenase mentioned earlier. It is generally (but not universally) true that NADPH is used largely in reductive syntheses, whereas NADH is more closely associated with energy metabolism. Furthermore, the transhydrogenase is involved in the oxidation of isocitric acid, since NADPH is formed in that reaction, but only NADH may be oxidized by the respiratory chain. The transhydrogenase reaction

$$NADH + NADP^+ \longrightarrow NAD^+ + NADPH$$

represents a simple transfer of hydrogen between two closely related compounds. There is little thermodynamic barrier to the reaction, as the potentials of the two are essentially the same. Since we have seen that there is a close relationship between potential, free energy change, and equilibrium, it is clear that there is no net energy requirement for the reaction (ΔF is 0) and the equilibrium constant is about 1. This means that at equilibrium there should be about an equal partition between NADH and NADPH, representing a balance which should be of importance to the cell. Recent measurements of the actual levels of reduction of NAD^+ and $NADP^+$ in intact mitochondria, however, reveal a very different picture. Under conditions where energy is available, NADPH is always found to be in a large excess over NADH, suggesting that energy is being used to push the reaction in that direction. Thus, under conditions where energy is available, hydrogen is shunted away from NADH, where it would mostly be used for production of further energy, toward NADPH where it is available for synthetic reactions. The transhydrogenase, then, may provide a means of coordinating two fundamental aspects of synthetic processes, the availability of energy and the generation of reducing power, while exerting a feedback inhibition on energy production itself.

Suggested Reading

CHANCE, B. (ed.), *Energy-linked Functions in Mitochondria*, Academic Press, New York, 1963.

GREEN, D. E., "The mitochondrial electron transfer system," in *Comprehensive Biochemistry*, M. Florkin and E. Stotz (eds.), Vol. 14, Elsevier, New York, 1966.

KEILIN, D., *The History of Cell Respiration and Cytochrome*, Cambridge University Press, Cambridge, 1966.

LEHNINGER, A. L., *Bioenergetics*, W. A. Benjamin, New York, 1965.

RACKER, E., *Mechanisms in Bioenergetics*, Academic Press, New York, 1965.

SLATER, E. C., "Oxidative phosphorylation," in *Comprehensive Biochemistry*, M. Florkin and E. Stotz (eds.), Vol. 14, Elsevier, New York, 1966.

CHAPTER 7

Energy Transfer Involving Light

Light is the ultimate source of most of the energy entering the living world. Members of the Plant Kingdom (as well as some bacteria) possess highly organized systems for the absorption of light and the utilization of the energy thus absorbed for the processes of life. Organisms exist that are able to reverse the process in a sense by emitting light produced through the use of chemical energy.

The process whereby radiant energy is converted to a chemical form of energy, leading to the synthesis of cell material, is called *photosynthesis*. Historically, the study of photosynthesis has passed through a number of phases, each centering on one aspect of the process believed to be fundamental at the time. Early studies of photosynthesis saw it as the light-induced production of carbohydrates and the process was usually summarized by the equation

$$CO_2 + H_2O \xrightarrow{\text{light, chlorophyll}} [CH_2O] + O_2$$

a formulation based on the fact that CO_2 was known to be taken up, oxygen was observed to be evolved, and carbohydrate (here abbreviated CH_2O) was the chief storage product in green plants. This view, according to which photosynthesis was just a special light-requiring type of sugar synthesis, was entirely consistent with the information then available.

However, in the 1930s additional information led to the questioning of the universal applicability of the above equation. For one thing, photosynthesis was discovered in several groups of bacteria, often involving quite different reactants. For example, some photosynthetic bacteria utilize hydrogen sulfide instead of water and yield sulfur instead of oxygen. In such cases the equation would be written

$$CO_2 + 2H_2S \xrightarrow{\text{light, chlorophyll}} [CH_2O] + 2S + H_2O$$

It will be observed that both sorts of photosynthesis include two basic processes, one being the formation of carbohydrate from CO_2, the other being an oxidation, in one case that of water to form oxygen, in the other that of H_2S to elementary sulfur. Furthermore, from everything that we know about synthetic reactions, the production of carbohydrate is likely to involve two separate requirements, that of energy and of

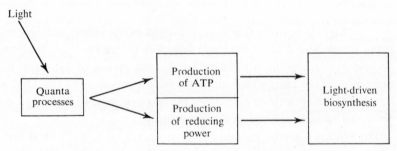

Figure 7–1. *Photosynthesis: a flow diagram.*

reducing power (electrons). The apparent complexity of photosynthesis may be resolved by considering the total process to be the sum of several interconnected, equally fundamental events illustrated in the flow diagram of Figure 7–1. In the diagram, "quanta processes" are those aspects of light absorption and energy transfer that are not chemical. A useful test is the ability of the truly quantum processes to take place at very low temperature, such as that of liquid nitrogen, conditions under which chemical reactions would be infinitely slow. It will be seen below that ATP production and the formation of reducing power are aspects of the same thing and that the two are equally necessary for the synthesis of carbohydrates.

Chlorophyll and the quantum processes

The compound responsible for most of the energy-trapping light absorption of both plants and photosynthetic bacteria is chlorophyll. Like the cytochromes, it is a porphyrin compound, but instead of the iron of cytochromes it contains a magnesium atom bound in the center of the ring system:

Two different chlorophylls (a and b) are known in plant cells, and a number of others are found in photosynthetic bacteria, all having the Mg-porphyrin ring system shown above with differing substituents on the ring. In addition, carotenoids are able to absorb light energy in photosynthesis, but the carotenoid molecules act in a secondary manner with respect to chlorophyll in that the energy must first be transferred to a chlorophyll molecule before further "fixation" of the energy can take place. The importance of carotenoid light absorption is probably related to the fact that green chlorophyll and yellow carotenoids absorb in different regions of the spectrum and so enable the cell to use a wider wavelength range in energy trapping.

It is obvious that, for light to produce an effect on cells, it must be absorbed. The region of the spectrum of interest in photosynthesis is that of visible light (or near-infrared in the case of bacteria), which represents interaction between quanta and the electronic energy levels of molecules. When such absorption takes place, a quantum of light produces an excitation in the molecule, wherein an electron is removed to a higher energy level. The energy available is given by the familiar expression

$$E = h\frac{c}{\lambda}$$

where E is the energy of a light quantum, c the velocity of light (a constant), h Planck's constant, and λ the wavelength of the light quantum. Thus the amount of energy available in photosynthesis is dependent on the wavelength, and it is likely that most of the infrared region, because of its lower energy, is not important in photosynthesis. Similarly, the greater energies of the shorter wavelength ultraviolet region are not photosynthetically important, inasmuch as they produce such dramatic changes in a large number of organic molecules as to be lethal to the cell. It is for this reason that UV light is used to kill micro-organisms, and cells, generally, do well to be as opaque to UV quanta as possible.

The absorption of light by chlorophyll leads to an electron being raised to a higher energy level, representing the primary excitation of photosynthesis. The energy may then be conserved in some chemical reaction—say, using the electron in a reduction, or the energy may become dissipated as heat or some form of reradiation (such as fluorescence) as it returns to its ground state. The considerable variety of ways whereby the electron may return to its lower state in the chlorophyll molecule makes it a useful system for studying absorption and re-emission processes in general, a fact which probably accounts for the recent influx of molecular physicists into the area. Pure biology is, however, more interested in the fate of the electron where reemission does not take place, and we must turn next to the history of the electron as it relates to energy production.

Electron transfer in photosynthesis

The reader is reminded of our central dogma about energy capture in cells: It always occurs by moving electrons. We have just said that the photosynthetic absorption of light (or indeed any photochemical process) involves the excitation of an electron to a higher energy level. It is consistent with everything we know to say that that electron may be regarded as a reductant, and that it passes along a series of oxidation-reduction compounds in a manner quite similar to the oxidation of a substrate by the respiratory chain. One might say that excited chlorophyll was acting as a substrate in the same sense as the intermediates of the Krebs cycle provide electrons to the mitochondrial respiratory chain.

The situation is rather more complicated than that found in respiration, as there appear to be at least two processes superimposed on each other, and we are not sure just how many light-requiring processes there

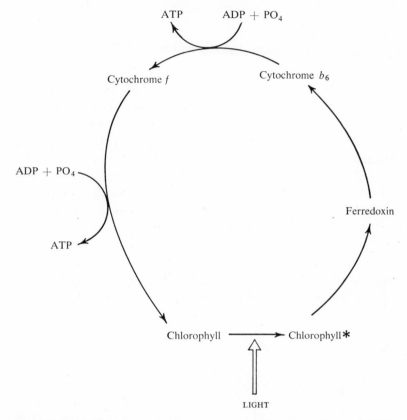

Figure 7-2. *The path of electrons in cyclic photophosphorylation.* Chlorophyll* *denotes an "activated" chlorophyll molecule (see text).*

are. In any case, one pathway for electron flow is shown in Figure 7–2 (*cyclic photophosphorylation*), in which the electron follows a closed cycle, finally passing back to the ground-state chlorophyll molecule. It will be noted that several electron carriers are involved (and others, including a quinone similar to ubiquinone) are also becoming implicated. Cytochrome b_6 is spectroscopically related to the mitochondrial cytochrome b, and f is similar to c. It is interesting that antimycin inhibits between the two, as in the mitochondrial situation. Ferredoxin is a nonheme iron protein, and there is evidence for such compounds in mitochondria. Finally, ATP formation is coupled to electron transfer, just as it is in the respiratory chain, and the synthesis is sensitive to certain uncoupling agents.

Formation of reducing power

But energy is not the only requirement for the syntheses leading to manufacture of cell material. Reducing power is also needed for the many reductive synthetic steps and photosynthesis provides a mechanism for its provision. One might imagine that the electron "ejected" from chlorophyll might be used as a reductant in this sense, but the situation is not that simple, since chlorophyll does not have an infinite supply of electrons, and, once ejected, the electron would be lost forever. A clue to the solution that cells have evolved in response to this problem is found in the demonstration (using tracer studies) that the oxygen produced by photosynthesis in green plants originates in water. The production of oxygen from water is essentially an oxidation and therefore must be accompanied by a reduction. The reduction in this case turns out to be that of biosynthesis; its pathway is outlined in Figure 7–3. The oxidation of water to form molecular oxygen includes the

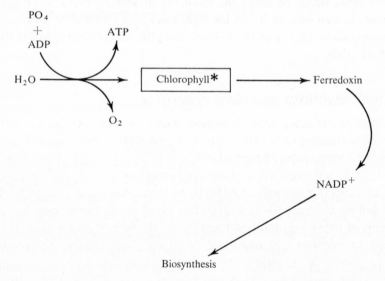

Figure 7–3. *The path of electrons in noncyclic photophosphorylation.*

removal of an electron which passes to chlorophyll. Activated chlorophyll in this instance serves as a pump causing the electron to be ejected to ferredoxin, which in turn reduces $NADP^+$. NADPH, as stated previously, is often the primary reducing agent and is essential in the formation of carbohydrate in photosynthetic organisms (see the next section). This noncyclic mode of electron transport is also associated with ATP formation but with one-half the yield of cyclic photophosphorylation. The mechanism of noncyclic ATP synthesis is not well understood, nor is the precise manner in which oxygen is evolved. It is important to note that oxygen evolution requires hydrogen ion production to account for the rest of the water molecule, and at least part of the hydrogen ion produced is used in the reduction of $NADP^+$, which involves the addition of both an electron and H^+ to the molecule. The importance of H^+ in photosynthesis has been recently exhibited by the demonstration of ATP synthesis coupled to pH changes in chloroplasts in the dark, a matter discussed in Chapter 8 in connection with transport across membranes.

This formulation of noncyclic photophosphorylation with chlorophyll serving as a pump reminds one of earlier views of photosynthesis that had light serving to promote the "photolysis" of water directly. This view, which predated the discovery of photosynthetic ATP synthesis, is seen now to be on the right track, but incomplete, as it said nothing about energy production or about the role of chlorophyll in the whole affair.

Light reactions and dark reactions

Both the primary light absorption events and the electron transport reactions leading to $NADP^+$ reduction and ATP synthesis require light for their occurrence. The actual synthesis of hexose is a "dark reaction" —light is not required if there are sources of energy and reducing equivalents (for example, NADPH). As far as mechanism is concerned, carbohydrate synthesis is a secondary event in photosynthesis, but in terms of physiology (and ecology) it is of the utmost importance. It is such an obvious and important result of photosynthesis that early students of photosynthesis saw nothing but the "fixation" of carbon dioxide to form sugar and assumed this reaction to be the whole story.

The pathway for carbohydrate synthesis by green plants is largely a reversal of glycolysis. The early steps of the series were demonstrated in elegant experiments in which algae were incubated with radioactive CO_2 and then plunged into boiling ethanol after a short interval in the

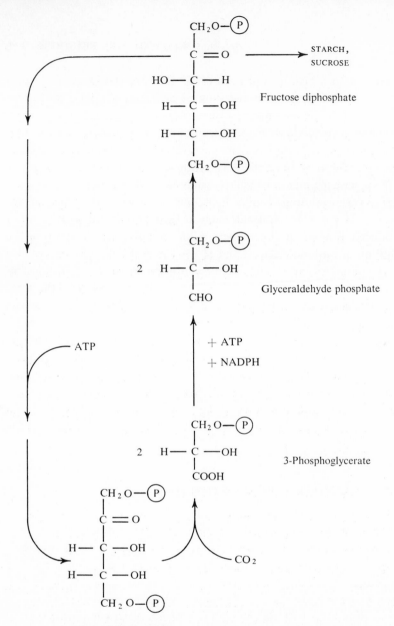

Figure 7–4. *An outline of photosynthetic carbon dioxide incorporation. The cycle is greatly simplified, omitting the extremely complex series of rearrangements leading to regeneration of ribulose diphosphate. It is likely that there is a six-carbon intermediate formed by the addition of CO_2 to ribulose diphosphate, which is rapidly cleaved to form two molecules of phosphoglycerate. Note that the reactions between phosphoglycerate and glucose are essentially those of glycolysis run in reverse.*

light. The plant extracts were then examined by paper chromatography to see which intracellular compounds were the ones first labeled. It turned out that 3-phosphoglycerate was the earliest compound to become radioactive, but that a number of sugars were labeled soon thereafter. On the basis of such experiments, a cyclic process for CO_2 incorporation was described, involving as its initial reaction the fusion of CO_2 and the 5-carbon sugar, ribulose diphosphate:

$$
\begin{array}{c}
CH_2O\textcircled{P} \\
| \\
C{=}O \\
| \\
H{-}C{-}OH \\
| \\
H{-}C{-}OH \\
| \\
CH_2O\textcircled{P}
\end{array}
\quad
\xrightarrow{\;CO_2\;}
\quad
2
\begin{array}{c}
CH_2O\textcircled{P} \\
| \\
CHOH \\
| \\
COOH
\end{array}
$$

The product of this reaction, two molecules of 3-carbon phospho-glycerate, will be familiar as a member of the glycolytic pathway. The reaction does not require light nor any of the products of photosythesis (ATP or NADPH). The subsequent use of phosphoglycerate to syn-thesize sugars proceeds by way of the pathway shown in Figure 7–4 and requires both ATP and NADPH—illustrating the obligatory nature of the connection between photosynthesis and CO_2 incorporation. Without becoming too involved in the complexity of the pathway, it is worth noting that most of its reactions are found in animal tissue as well, and the reason the pathway is associated with photosynthesis is because of the requirements for ATP and NADPH. Indeed it used to be thought that CO_2 fixation was a unique property of green plants, but recently a number of different reactions incorporating CO_2 into organic compounds in animal cells have been discovered. These are, however, rather minor routes in animal cells, whereas CO_2 accounts for all carbon in the biosyntheses of many plants under many conditions.

Control of photosynthesis through regulation of pigment synthesis

Since the photosynthetic pigments are at the heart of the whole affair, it is reasonable that the formation of the pigments themselves might be a locus of control. Photosynthetic organisms live under a variety of conditions of nutrient and illumination, and it is necessary that the rate of photosynthetic energy trapping reflect the situation at hand. For example, it is well known that seedlings grown under conditions where photosynthesis is impossible (in the dark) do not form the photosynthetic apparatus, which includes chlorophyll and accessory pigments. If such *etiolated* plants are placed in the light, the concentration of pigments soon reaches a normal value.

Much of the most compelling information about control of photosynthesis comes from studies of microorganisms, which are useful subjects because of the possibility of controlled culture and homogenous populations. Unicellular algae such as *Chlamydomonas or Euglena* may be grown in pure culture, and the concentration of pigment in such cells is proportional to light intensity over a considerable range. Similar results are noted with the photosynthetic bacterium, *Rhodopseudomonas*, and it is interesting that there appears to be an optimum light intensity for pigment synthesis. Thus cells grown aerobically in the dark make no pigment, cells grown in dim light do, and in bright light synthesis again is suppressed. This should be regarded as an adaption whereby cells contain maximum pigment under those conditions where the absorption of radiant energy is most critical—conditions of minimal illumination.

Cells of *Rhodopseudomonas* are able to grow aerobically in the dark in the presence of organic substrates using respiratory electron transport for energy production. It is interesting that the presence of oxygen suppresses pigment production completely, so that dividing cells soon exhibit much lower concentrations of chlorophyll and carotenoids. Thus in this instance the availability of oxygen—which allows oxidative phosphorylation—serves to eliminate the apparatus for photosynthetic ATP synthesis, a situation analogous to the Pasteur effect, where the fermentative route to ATP synthesis is turned off. One might suppose that oxidative ATP formation represents the most efficient form of energy trapping by cells and that nature prefers to use it where possible. Obviously, oxygen does not eliminate photosynthesis in the case of higher plants, because, unlike the photosynthetic bacteria, green plants are commonly found in aerobic situations (such as my flower box). Indeed, the aerobic character of our planet is largely caused by the fact that green plants evolve oxygen as a photosynthetic by-product—and it is obvious that oxygen-induced repression of photosynthesis in higher plants would lead to ecological disaster.

Biological emission of light

Cells generally are able to give off electromagnetic radiation, and its release is coupled to the chemical reactions within the cell. In most instances, the radiation is in the infrared region and might be described as metabolic heat production. In some cases widely dispersed in the plant and animal kingdoms, the radiation produced is of sufficiently high energy to fall within the visible region of the spectrum and is termed *bioluminescence*. Bioluminescence does not involve a reversal of photosynthesis, since it is found in nonphotosynthetic organisms (such as fireflies), but it shows some interesting similarities.

What is known of the mechanism of light production suggests that it should be thought of as a special case of *chemiluminescence*, which is the release of energy in the form of light in the course of a chemical reaction. As most chemical reactions in the cell are catalyzed by enzymes, it is no surprise that the luminescent reaction requires the presence of an enzyme which is called, somewhat poetically, *luciferase*. Luciferase is actually a class of enzymes, the members of which catalyze the light-producing oxidation of any one of a number of substrates, depending on the phylogenetic source of the system. In the firefly, the substrate is a complex organic molecule,

called *luciferin*. The oxidation of luciferin to yield light and the involvement of ATP in the whole affair is summarized by the following reactions:

1. Luciferin + ATP $\longrightarrow$ AMP-luciferin + $\textcircled{P}$–$\textcircled{P}$
2. Luciferin-AMP + $\frac{1}{2}O_2$ $\longrightarrow$ AMP-oxidized luciferin + H_2O
3. Oxidized luciferin-AMP $\longrightarrow$ Oxidized luciferin + AMP + light

For the process to be truly cyclic, a means must be at hand where oxidized luciferin can become reduced again. In bacterial luminescence, the reducing agent appears to be a flavoprotein which, as seen in Chapter

6, receives electrons from the primary substrates of respiration, such as succinate and NADH:

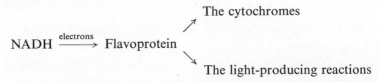

It is interesting to note that, although the details of mechanism are not yet completely worked out in the various luminescent organisms, the general features are suggestive of a process rather like photosynthesis run backward. Photosynthesis is light absorption coupled to the formation of ATP and reducing power, while the light-producing systems appear to *require* ATP (or energy-coupled respiration) and reducing power (in the form of a reduced flavin in bacteria) for light to be emitted. The details of the two processes, however, differ significantly in a number of obvious ways, including the nature of the quantum events, structures involved, and their phylogenetic distribution.

Suggested Reading

CALVIN, M., and BASSHAM, J. A., *The Photosynthesis of Carbon Compounds*, W. A. Benjamin, New York, 1962.

CLAYTON, R., *Molecular Physics in Photosynthesis*, Ginn (Blaisdell), Boston, 1965.

HILL, R., and C. P. WHITTINGHAM, *Photosynthesis*, Methuen & Co., London, 1957.

KAMEN, M. D., *Primary Processes in Photosynthesis*, Academic Press, New York, 1963.

MCELROY, W. D., and GLASS B. (eds.), *A Symposium on Light and Life*, Johns Hopkins Press, Baltimore, 1961.

CHAPTER 8

Membranes and Cell Compartmentation

In Chapter 1 we saw that the structure of cells is very much a matter of membranes, with systems of them enclosing the cell, isolating the nucleus from the rest of the interior, and filling the interior with complex structures (organelles). Not only do membranes constitute the units from which much of cell structure is built, but they play an essential role in cell activities and, most especially, in the regulation of those activities. Cells not only fail to look like a bag of enzymes, but they do not act as if they were. Many of the most interesting properties of cells, such as irritability and transport, are uniquely associated with membranes, while many of the metabolic reactions of cells take place on membrane surfaces. The compartments formed by membranes within the cell, thus separating potential reactants, have profound significance for the pattern of metabolism. Clearly, the ability of membranes to allow selective passage of some compounds, but not others, and to couple the passage of some with energy-yielding reactions, presents significant possibilities for regulation.

Membrane structure

The membranes of the cell have certain properties in common, whether they constitute the outer boundary of the cell or form the organelles of its interior. All are composed almost entirely of protein and lipid, and all have a similar geometry—that of double layers with over-all dimensions of about 75 angstroms.* Superimposed upon this basic pattern is considerable variation, depending on intracellular location and function. For example, the mitochondrion is bounded by a membrane about 250 angstroms thick, which is composed, in most regions, of two roughly 75-angstrom double membranes separated by about 100 angstroms. Likewise, the surface membrane of such cells as muscle includes the same double membrane but with an additional outer layer probably composed, at least in part, of collagen. Indeed, in such structures there is some question as to where the outer surface of the membrane terminates, since the outermost portion may be continuous with extracellular connective tissue elements. In any case, the characteristic double-layered structure does form a significant part of cell membranes generally and might be taken to suggest a unity of composition and probably also function.

The chemical composition of membranes presents a similar picture to the structure in that considerable variation between cell types is superimposed on a common pattern. All membranes studied are composed almost entirely of lipid and protein, with much of the lipid in the form of phospholipids. Membranes from mammalian tissue contain steroids, including cholesterol, whereas bacterial membranes do not. In addition, myelin membranes from the nervous tissue of animals contain α-hydroxy fatty acids, which are not found elsewhere. It is probable that, as more detailed information about membrane composition becomes available, additional differences will be discovered. When one considers that different membranes play distinct roles in energy metabolism, transport of small molecules, and protein synthesis, as well as other processes, it becomes clear that considerable variation might be expected.

Models for membrane properties

Discovery, by means of electron microscopy, of the ubiquity of double membrane structures, as well as the knowledge that membranes are composed of protein and lipid, has encouraged students of the cell to seek explanations for membrane structure in possible geometric relationships between the two. The discovery of artificial systems which appear to duplicate some properties of biological membranes has suggested to

* That is, 75×10^{-8} cm.

some workers that the formation of membranes occurs by way of relatively simple intermolecular interactions. A mixture of purified phospholipids and water forms aggregations (or micelles) which can be of a tubular nature, apparently composed of a double layer of molecules with a separation very roughly that of natural membranes (50 to 100 angstroms). Such similarities have suggested that model systems may lead to detailed understanding of natural membranes, but it is likely that considerable caution should be exercised. For example, the spacing between the layers in micelles is not constant, with great variation associated with the method of preparation and the concentration of dissolved ions. Thus at least one of the similarities between artificial and biological systems may be due to a fortuitous selection of conditions.

On the other hand, micelles of various compositions are known to exhibit a dynamic shape and size, with the possibility of coalescence to form larger aggregates. In this property they are similar to cell membranes, which likewise appear able to coalesce and change configuration. There are many instances of fusion of parts of intracellular membranes, of which a good example is the closure of the animal cell membrane after furrowing associated with mitosis. When mitochondria are disrupted by addition of detergent or by ultrasonic vibrations, the outer membrane appears to fragment, and the pieces roll up and coalesce in the form of closed spheres which retain some of their original permeability properties. Perhaps the most important lesson to be gained in studies of model systems is related to this great fluidity of membranes, giving a transient aspect to the whole of cell structure.

Passage of water through cell membranes

Biological membranes are generally quite permeable to water. For example, when red blood cells are placed in solutions of low solute content (hypotonic), they take up water from the medium with consequent swelling. Similarly, cell organelles such as chloroplasts or mitochondria swell or contract depending on the content of the medium in which they find themselves, indicating that such organelles with closed outer surfaces also allow water to pass readily through their membranes. As a consequence of this property, techniques for the isolation of cells and cell organelles must include the careful selection of a medium with precisely the correct solute concentration to avoid osmotic disruption of membrane structure.

The passage of water across a membrane into a region of higher solute concentration may be viewed in terms of chemical equilibrium. The equilibrium position in such situations is that which most closely approaches equal concentrations of solute on each side of the membrane. That is to say, a concentration difference in adjacent regions of space is an inherently unstable (improbable) arrangement and the system tends to approach the configuration of highest probability attainable. Since a membrane is often much more permeable to water than to a given solute, it follows that the equilibration of concentration must involve a net transfer of water toward the region of higher solute concentration. From this argument, it should be clear that the selection of a solute in a medium for isolation of an organelle should be governed by the permeability of the membrane to that solute. For example, both the sugars sucrose and mannitol are unable to penetrate the mitochondrial outer membrane, and both are used in media for such isolations.

Osmotic pressure

When the space on one side of a membrane is constrained in volume, it is possible for the force of water flow in the direction of higher solute concentration to exert a pressure (see Figure 8–1). The pressure (osmotic pressure) may be detected under conditions where there is no net transfer of water. Pressure exerted in this manner is defined under conditions of very low solute concentration as

$$\pi = mRT$$

where π is the osmotic pressure in atmospheres, R the gas constant (82 ml-atm/mole-degree) and T the absolute temperature. The concentration, m, is in terms of moles per milliliter and provides a way of using the relationship to estimate the molecular weights of impermeant molecules by means of osmometers employing an artificial membrane. This technique has been used for the determination of protein molecular weight according to the following equation, obtained directly from the preceding one:

$$M = \frac{cRT}{\pi}$$

where M is the molecular weight and c the concentration in grams per milliliter. This is valid only for low concentrations. It is plain from the

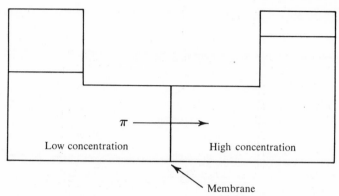

Figure 8–1. *Generation of osmotic pressure (π) by a difference in solute concentration across a membrane.*

inclusion of the absolute temperature and the gas constant in these equations that osmotic pressure is a thermodynamic affair, a conclusion also consistent with the origin of the phenomenon in an approach to equilibrium.

Aside from its utility in molecular-weight calculations, osmotic pressure plays an important role in the biological world in providing rigidity to a number of structures. It is probably osmotic pressure that keeps most closed membrane structures (including cells and organelles) from collapsing. It is likely that such structures retain their shape due to the opposition of a small osmotic force to the slight elastic force of the membrane. However, constant structure is maintained only over very narrow ranges of concentration, as the membranes are far from rigid, and significant changes give rise to deformation. On the other hand, some membranes, most notably cell membranes of higher plants and bacteria, are enclosed within inelastic cell walls, to which osmotic pressure applies them closely (Figure 8–2). The role of osmotic pressure in such cases may be exhibited when plant cells such as those of Elodea are placed in a hypertonic medium (one where the relevant solute concentration is higher outside the cell). Water passes from the cell to the medium, and the loss of pressure is seen in the formation of spaces between the cell membrane and wall. This phenomenon is called plasmolysis. An additional demonstration of the importance of osmotic pressure is seen in the fact that bacteria are exceedingly durable when enclosed within their cell walls at appropriate external solute concentrations, so that great forces are required for their disruption. However, the

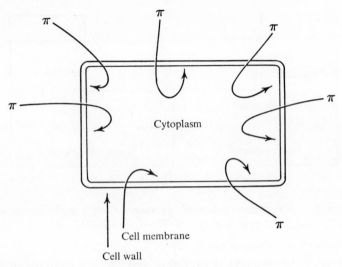

Figure 8–2. *Osmotic pressure (π) providing rigidity in plant (or bacterial) cells by forcing the membrane against the cell wall.*

walls of certain bacteria are digested by a specific enzyme (lysozyme) which renders them fragile and sensitive to changes in the suspension medium. This osmotic sensitivity of bacteria lacking cell walls has been the basis for measurements of the passage of the sugar, lactose, into cells of *Escherichia coli*. In such studies, it is possible to detect the increase in intracellular sugar, monitoring the increased cell volume by measuring the optical density of cell suspensions. An important finding was that sugar which had entered the cell was osmotically active, implying that it must be free in solution and not bound to the cell structure.

Selective permeability: the passage of solutes through membranes

The power of cellular membranes to regulate and specify cell events comes in part from the great selectivity of membranes with respect to different solutes. When such a membrane is interposed between two regions of space, it affects the free diffusion of some molecules to a very slight degree, and completely prevents that of others. The manner in which membranes exercise such selectivity is obviously related to the mechanism by which they transport solutes, and one might expect a membrane to exhibit one sort of selectivity if translocation was (for example) by pores and another if it occurred by means of solution of the solute in the lipid phase of the membrane. In fact, membranes act as if several different mechanisms were in effect, including the two mentioned.

Examples of membrane selectivity include both general and specific cases. One might say that, in general, large molecules encounter greater resistance in passing through membranes than do smaller ones. Similarly, molecules with a great dipolar character tend to pass through membranes with difficulty when compared to those with less. This is probably due to the formation of a shell of water molecules about the permeant molecule, which would result in increasing its effective cross section. In a similar fashion an asymmetric molecule presents on the average a greater cross section to a membrane and is less able to pass through it than a more symmetrical one of similar molecular weight.

As important as size in determining the permeability of a biological membrane to a given solute is the solubility of the solute in lipid. We say that lipid forms an important part of cellular membranes, and it is reasonable that a compound soluble in lipid should have an easier road through such membranes. For example, a common observation related to the study of inhibitors of mitochondrial processes is that such compounds become effective at lower concentrations, as homologues with longer and longer alphatic side chains are used. Since the longer side chains confer greater lipid solubility, such compounds are better able to traverse the mitochondrial membrane and produce their effect. The influence of lipid solubility is closely related to degree of ionization, which generally bears an inverse relationship to it.

In addition to certain general relationships between transport specificity and molecular size, shape, and lipid solubility, there are many examples of more detailed specificity, where a certain molecular structure or the presence of certain groups play a major role. This sort of discrimination by membranes is strongly reminiscent of enzyme specificity and suggests that membranes may bear sites related to the transport of specific molecules with, perhaps, a geometric relationship to the structure of the molecules. As an example of such selectivity, one might cite the transport of amino acids, which appear to require such sites. However, there is not a single mechanism for all amino acids, nor is there one for each different amino acid. Rather, there appear to be separate mechanisms (and sites) for the translocation of neutral amino acids (such as glycine), cationic (such as lysine), and anionic amino acids (such as glutamate). Evidence for the three groups comes from the fact that within each group amino acids may be shown to compete for a single site (since the addition of one will suppress the uptake of another), while such inhibition, which is similar to enzyme competitive inhibition, does not occur between members of different groups.

Although the apparent existence of specific sites points to similarities between membrane transport and enzyme activity, it is important to note that membrane specificity appears in many cases to be somewhat less restrictive. In other words, the groups of compounds that react at a certain site tend to be larger in the case of membranes, enabling a single site to mediate the entry of a number of compounds. Thus it is possible for one site to effect the entry of eight or ten amino acids, while a single enzyme with equal affinity for a number of different amino acid precursors might well generate numerous side pathways in metabolism and interfere seriously with metabolic control.

Transport mechanisms

It should be clear that the remarks made above about membrane specificity all bear a relation to the nature of mechanisms that might be involved. When one discusses the influence of molecular size and shape on transport, it is rather too easy to think of the membrane as bearing pores through which the molecules pass. Similarly, when one speaks of the importance of lipid solubility, the sort of mechanism that comes to mind involves the dissolution of the molecule into the lipid phase of the membrane. Finally, the discovery of precise chemical specificity in many cases has led to the idea of membrane transport sites analogous to the active site of an enzyme. One is thus free to choose among approaches to transport which seem to bear very little similarity and which, at first examination, appear somewhat mutually exclusive.

Fortunately, one does not have to choose, since real transport is probably a combination of a number of mechanisms. The apparent mutual exclusiveness of the mechanisms is diminished when one notes that membrane transport itself may be divided into a number of phases, including the passage of the molecule into the membrane, the traversing of the membrane, and the exit into the cell or organelle interior. It is quite possible that the different phases of transport may each contribute to the specificity of the process as a whole and that one or another of them may play a greater role depending on the nature of the solute molecule involved.

Several additional transport mechanisms have been suggested to account for specific properties of membranes. For example, studies of disaccharide transport by bacteria have led to the idea that transport may be effected by an enzyme termed a *permease* (see Chapter 4). The permease is believed to be a protein because its synthesis is prevented by known inhibitors of protein production such as chloramphenicol. Furthermore, it is an induced enzyme—it is synthesized in response to the presence of its substrate. It is likely that a bacterial permease is one instance of a more general phenomenon, transport mediated by a protein, and it is probably unfortunate that the term permease has been adopted, since it tends to set it apart and imply a distinction that may not exist.

The precise role of a protein in a transport event is not yet clear, but there appear to be a number of possibilities. It may be that conformational changes in a protein molecule are involved in the actual translocation. One might imagine a protein molecule situated in a cellular membrane and oriented in such a way that a conformational change (alteration in tertiary structure) would reorient the active site so that a small molecule bound to it would be brought close to the "inner" side of the membrane (see Figure 8–3). Similar mechanisms have been suggested to account for active transport coupled to the hydrolysis of ATP, whereby the binding of ATP would lead to such structural changes as to effect net transport of a different molecule.

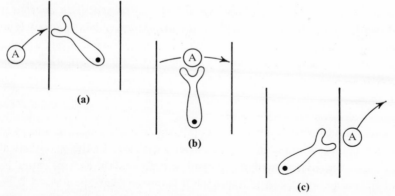

(a)

(b)

(c)

Figure 8–3. *Conformational change in a protein leading to transport across a membrane. This is a very diagrammatic view, where the binding of A to the transport protein produces a change in the orientation of the active site, bringing A to the other side of the membrane.*

An additional manner whereby a protein situated in a membrane could lead to translocation of a chemical group is illustrated in Figure 8–4. This mechanism, which was suggested by Mitchell and Moyle,

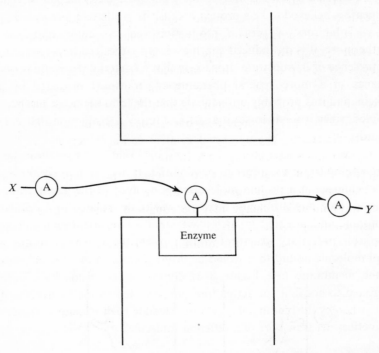

Figure 8–4. *A possible mechanism for group transport. An enzyme is shown to be located at a "pore" in the membrane. The membrane is so structured that the enzyme is accessible to X on the left and Y on the right. X is able to donate group A to the enzyme only from the left, while Y can pick it up only on the right, leading to a net translocation of A from left to right.*

requires an enzyme situated in a membrane with steric restrictions as to which reactants may approach it from each side. In the hypothetical example, the environment in the membrane around the enzyme would be such as to permit X—A to approach it from the "left" and Y—A from the "right." The sequence of transport might include X—A donating the A group to the enzyme, followed by the diffusion of X to the "left" (the only direction in which it is free to move). Y would then approach the active site and receive the A group. Y—A, being free to move only

toward the "right," would leave the site, giving rise to a net translocation of A from left to right. This mechanism has been very influential in
pointing out that the only requirement for translocation by an enzyme is
the sort of anisotropy suggested, and has led to some very specific
suggestions as to the relationship between energy production and
transport. It is important to realize that, although the mechanism seeks
to describe group translocation, it may be of great generality, since the
group A could represent a whole molecule, such as a sugar or amino
acid, bound to the carrier molecules, X and Y.

Additional examples of transport mechanisms include those involving
the coupled transport of more than one solute, either in the same or in
opposite directions. The uptake of divalent cations (such as Ca^{++} or
Sr^{++}) into mitochondria appears in many cases to be necessarily
coupled to the uptake of certain anions, including phosphate or acetate.
This is not merely a requirement for balance of charge, since there are
other ways in which charge may be equalized. One of these is the
extrusion of the positively charged hydrogen ion, which is also known to
occur as a response to mitochondrial ion transport. This extrusion

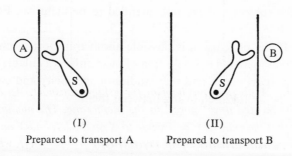

(I)   (II)

Prepared to transport A   Prepared to transport B

Figure 8–5. *A simple model for exchange transport. Site S is able to
transport A when it is oriented toward the left, B when toward the right.
Transport is imagined to take place through a conformational change in
the carrier protein, so that transport of either species will leave the carrier
positioned at the side of the membrane toward which transport has
occurred. When B is absent, and A is being transported, the carrier
returns to the left (so that it can pick up another molecule of A) by some
random process. When B is present the conformational change involved
in B transport will rapidly return the carrier toward the left and therefore
stimulate A transport. The presence of A will stimulate B transport in like
manner.*

represents a case of coupled ion transport in opposite directions, of which several other examples occur. Mechanisms have been devised to account for such exchange transport, of which a simple example is found in Figure 8–5. In it, the transport of A to the right is coupled to that of a similar molecule, B, to the left. We imagine the transport to be mediated by a protein bearing an active site free to move, perhaps because of conformational changes in the protein. When A is trans-located, it first binds to the site, S, and is carried on it to the right, where it is dumped. The site then eventually returns to the left side and picks up another A molecule. On the other hand, if there is a high concentration of B on the right side, and if B has a similar ability to bind to the site, then a net flow of B to the left will tend to promote the orientation of the site in the left direction. Thus it will tend to stimulate A transport by ensuring that the site will be, on the average, more able to receive A. To the external observer, the two fluxes will support each other and appear coupled.

The preceding examples represent only a few of the mechanisms that have been proposed to account for transport phenomena. They are included here to give an idea of the sort of thinking that is brought to bear on the subject and are not intended to be inclusive. For a more complete discussion, see the book by Christensen listed in Suggested Reading. If any conclusion is possible about transport mechanisms, it would be that there is a rich selection of mechanisms available to explain a given transport event, and that studies of specificity and competition are apt to be useful in choosing between them.

Energy requirements for transport

In our discussions of specificity and mechanism of transport thus far, energy requirements have not arisen. It should be clear, however, that the net movement of molecules from one space to another can require energy, and it is important to consider how such energy is applied.

In a sense, all transport requires energy and should be regarded as "active." For example, in many cases there is no requirement for meta-bolic energy, and one finds that the transport is from a direction of high solute concentration to one of low concentration. Thus the flux is with the concentration gradient and might be regarded as passive. However, the situation where a membrane divides two regions of differing con-centration should be regarded as one able to yield energy. The degree to which the concentrations differ from equilibrium is related to the energy available in the sense described in Chapter 2.

Thus it may be said that energy is always expended in the net transport of molecules or ions across a membrane and that the energy may be in the form of a concentration gradient or, if not, it must be supplied by other means.

The role of diffusion

Under conditions where membrane transport is favored by a concentration gradient, it is convenient to regard it as a special case of diffusion. If a region of space contains a solution in which there is a concentration gradient (a higher concentration in one part than another), it is well known that the gradient will tend to disappear as diffusion proceeds, leading to an equalization of concentration throughout the space. Since diffusion gives rise to a net flow of material and vanishes at equilibrium it is appropriate to think of it in the terms established in Chapter 2. It was said there that a flow, J, could be expressed as the product of a driving force, X, and a proportionality constant, L, or, more precisely, as the sum of all such products that might be relevant:

$$J = L_1 X_1 + L_2 X_2 + L_3 X_3 + \cdots$$

In the case of simple diffusion, J represents the transport of material through a unit area orthogonal to the direction of flow. In the simplest case (where there are no gradients of temperature or pressure) the driving force is simply the gradient in concentration dc/dx, where c is the concentration and x the distance in the direction of flow. The proportionality constant is expressed as D, the diffusion coefficient, yielding an expression

$$J = D\frac{dc}{dx}$$

which is valid for diffusion in the steady state (see Chapter 2). Steady state in this case means that the gradient is unchanging with respect to time, a condition that is probably often realized in cells where the gradient may be maintained by metabolic processes or by having a very large external volume. In the more general case of non-steady-state diffusion, the rate is proportional to the second derivative of concentration:

$$J = D \frac{d^2c}{dx^2}$$

These relations remain valid when diffusion takes place in regions of space between which a membrane is interposed. Although the membrane might be said to impose a resistance to flow, this might be expressed by an altered diffusion coefficient, and the rate would still be proportional to the gradient found in any given region. The special effects that might take place on and in the membrane, such as lipid solubilization or protein conformational changes, should probably be regarded as perturbations of the most general cases described above. Unfortunately for detailed analysis, the precise measurement of a gradient within a membrane is not readily accessible and only an average gradient may be estimated. Similarly, the relevant gradient might be that of a complex between the permeant molecule and a carrier, and this is not easily determined. Such cases, where the driving force is that of diffusion but the actual transport is mediated by a chemical mechanism in the membrane, are called *facillated diffusion*, and appear often.

Translocation of solutes against a concentration gradient

Many membranes are known to translocate molecules or ions into regions of higher concentration than at their source. Cells and closed organelles are able to effect the concentration of solutes until very high internal concentrations are reached and very considerable gradients are established. Cultured mammalian cells are able to concentrate a number of solutes, including amino acids, until the total gradient across the membrane is of the order of 0.1 M. Mitochondria are able to take up calcium and phosphate until the mitochondrial structure is actually deformed by the precipitated calcium phosphate inside, which can equal about 20 per cent of the mitochondrial mass. In these cases (and numerous others) transport is opposed to considerable concentration gradients, and clearly a process other than pure diffusion must be available to supply energy. Such a translocation, where energy is supplied by a process which is not identical to the translocation, is usually termed *active transport*.

In describing active transport, it is first necessary to point out that there are many situations in which a "passive" diffusion-linked process might appear active, and one must be extremely careful to exclude them. For example, binding sites within a closed membrane might lead to an apparent concentration of solute by removing it from solution as soon as it passed into the interior (see Figure 8–6). Thus, as long as binding

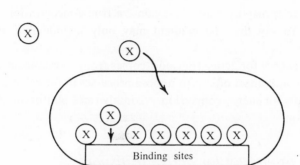

Figure 8–6. *Apparently active transport due to internal binding. Binding lowers the internal concentration of free X and so promotes, by mass action, its entry.*

sites held out, the transport would take place against what would look to the external observer like a concentration gradient. Similarly, transport followed by spontaneous utilization of the transported molecule would allow apparent concentration, unless one were careful to examine the chemical nature of the material after it had entered, a matter frequently overlooked when transport is followed by monitoring the uptake of radioactive solute. In fact, such a process might be regarded as a type of active translocation, because it is a special case of a thermodynamically unfavorable process (the uptake) which is coupled to a spontaneous one.

It is also possible to think of situations in which a transport process operating against a gradient might be coupled to one in the opposing direction that is favored by diffusion. Thus it has been suggested that the transport of some organic molecules, including amino acids and monosaccharides, might be coupled in some way to cation transport. The evidence for this includes a significant influence of cation distribution on transport of the organic molecule.

Although a number of processes can give rise to transport which appears active in that it runs "uphill" against a concentration gradient, the term active transport is usually more restricted in usage. It appears that active translocating systems in membranes often have a great deal in common, even though a wide variety of molecules or ions may be involved. For our purposes, we shall describe active transport as having two necessary aspects, which, together, serve as sort of a definition:

1. Active transport must run against a true concentration gradient, which is to say that the gradient may only include free, unbound, species.

2. The energy for active transport comes from spontaneous reactions of the cell, and, most often, from those processes in the cell most closely associated with energy conversion—oxidative and photosynthetic phosphorylation.

Source of energy for active transport

In general, energy for active membrane translocation comes from those processes in the chemistry of the cell which are associated with ATP production. Thus it is not surprising that active transport by aerobic cells is greatly inhibited by dinitrophenol, which was seen earlier to be an uncoupler of ATP synthesis, and by cyanide, which inhibits respiration itself. Similarly, in cells which are unable to trap energy by aerobic processes and which rely on glycolysis, transport against a gradient is inhibited by reagents which interfere with glycolytic ATP production. Finally, transport by photosynthetic cells (and their organelles) is linked to light absorption and the related energy-transferring processes, exactly as one might predict. These observations suggest that inhibition of a transport process by, for example, dinitrophenol, yields a valid test of whether transport is active and implies that ATP, the synthesis of which is prevented by dinitrophenol, is the source of the energy. In fact, dinitrophenol, at least at high concentrations, produces side effects which are able to interfere even with diffusion-linked transport of some solutes, so that one should not attempt to use inhibition by it as a single criterion. Furthermore, the fact that dinitrophenol interferes with both oxidative ATP formation and with certain transport events does not necessarily imply that ATP is itself the energy carrier. This is clear on recalling that the synthesis of ATP appears to occur by way of high-energy intermediates, which are themselves formed as a result of respiratory electron transfer:

$$\text{Respiration} \longrightarrow \begin{array}{c} \text{High-energy} \\ \text{intermediates} \end{array} \nearrow \begin{array}{c} \text{ATP} \\ \text{ADP} \\ + \\ PO_4 \end{array}$$

Since dinitrophenol is usually thought of as either preventing the formation of the intermediates or leading to their destruction, it is possible that the intermediates are the sources of energy for transport and that there is no absolute requirement for ATP. Note that the role of ATP might even be to lead to the formation of the intermediates by reversal of the last set of reactions. Evidence for transport that does not require ATP *per se* comes from studies of mitochondrial ion uptake, which requires energy from respiration to cross steep gradients. The inhibitor, oligomycin, which acts between the intermediates and ATP formation, is without effect on ion uptake when the energy is obtained from respiration. Under similar conditions, dinitrophenol eliminates transport completely. On the other hand, uptake may occur without respiration (as in the presence of cyanide), as long as ATP is supplied in the reaction mixture. This ATP-dependent ion transport is, however, eliminated by oligomycin, which suggests that the intermediates, and not ATP itself, are the direct sources of transport power. These results are summarized in Figure 8–7, and indicate that one might expect competition for the intermediates between ATP synthesis and transport, and this is found to be the case. Thus the addition of Ca^{++} to a mitochondrial suspension inhibits ATP synthesis markedly, indicating that Ca^{++} is able to compete quite well for the intermediates. Note that high-energy intermediates might be expected to play an especially significant role in mitochondrial transport, owing to the fact that they are presumably formed there. Nothing is known about the permeability of the mitochondrial membrane to the intermediates and, indeed, one view of their nature holds such "permeability" to be self-contradictory.

Since mitochondrial ion uptake, at least, is dependent on the use of high-energy intermediates, it is reasonable to suppose that ion uptake should lead to their breakdown and, therefore, should stimulate respiration in a manner similar to an uncoupler such as dinitrophenol (see

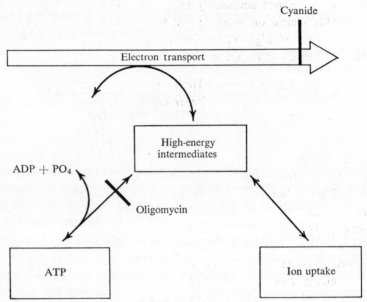

Figure 8–7. *Energy pathways for mitochondrial ion uptake. Transport depends on the presence of high-energy intermediates which may be formed as a result of electron transport or generated from added ATP. It is possible to examine the two sources of intermediates separately, as cyanide prevents their formation by one route and oligomycin by the other. When energy is being supplied by electron transport, the reactions of ATP synthesis and those of ion uptake compete for the high-energy intermediates formed.*

Chapter 5). This is true, and Figure 8–8 shows the effect of added calcium on mitochondrial respiration in the absence of ADP. Without ADP, mitochondria cannot make ATP, and the intermediates build up, a condition which was seen previously to lead to a less than maximum rate of respiration. It is interesting to note that certain estuarine organisms that are able to carry on transport of ions in response to changes in salinity do so by means of a process which is accompanied by an increase in the respiratory rate of the entire organism.

It will be seen later that the nature of the high-energy intermediates which we have found to be implicated in mitochondrial transport is, to say the very least, unclear. Not only is the precise chemical nature of such "compounds" still undiscovered, but it has been suggested that the intermediates are not chemical entities at all, but rather gradients of one

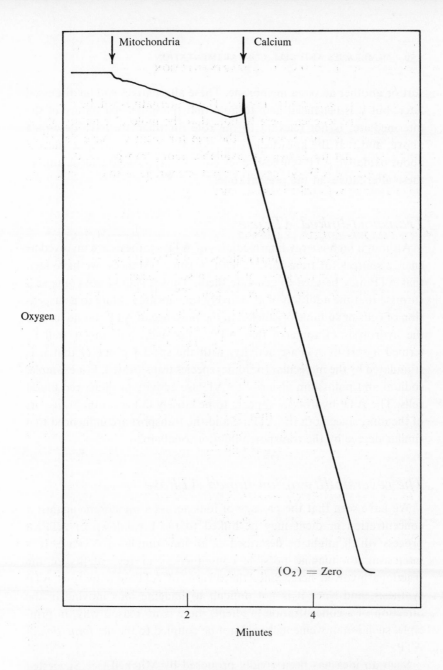

Figure 8–8. *Stimulation of mitochondrial respiration by calcium. This is a record produced by a polarographic electrode sensitive to oxygen. The reaction mixture included phosphate buffer, magnesium chloride, succinate, and water. When calcium (as CaCl₂) is added, respiration is greatly increased, and independent measurements using a radioactive isotope of calcium show that calcium is concentrated within the mitochondria.*

sort or another across a membrane. These alternatives will be discussed later, but it is beneficial here to note that the molecular nature of the intermediates is not relevant to the role for them we have described above, and that the knowledge available about transport and, indeed, about oxidative ATP synthesis does not encourage us to choose among these alternatives at the present time.

Transport-linked ATPase

Although high-energy intermediates of ATP synthesis are involved as energy sources for transport, at least in some instances, we have seen that ATP may be used to generate them. Thus it should not come as a surprise that the addition of an actively translocated solute to a suspension of cells or suitable organelles in the presence of ATP should lead to the hydrolysis of some of that ATP. This hydrolysis might well be termed a sort of ATPase activity, with the special property that it is stimulated by the molecular (or ionic) species translocated. For example, sodium and potassium give rise to ATPase activity in intact red blood cells. The ATP hydrolysis appears to be closely linked to the transport of the ions, since both the ATPase and the transport are influenced to a similar degree by the transport inhibitor, ouabain.

The reversibility of ion-linked ATPase

We have seen that the passage of ions across a membrane against a concentration gradient may be linked to the breakdown of ATP, a process which might be described as an ion-stimulated ATPase. It is interesting to imagine possible consequences of reversibility of the reactions involved here. Since the reverse of ATPase activity is ATP synthesis, and since it is not difficult to imagine ions moving in the direction of a concentration gradient, there is no reason why, in principle, such ion movement should not be coupled to the net *formation* of ATP.

Such an idea has been vividly proposed by Mitchell (see Suggested Reading) to account for mitochondrial ATP synthesis coupled to electron transport. This suggestion has had the effect of throwing the whole idea of high-energy *chemical* intermediates into question and has emphasized very strongly the vectoral nature of many energy-linked processes. Mitchell has noted that ATP synthesis in mitochondria and chloroplasts appears to require an intact organelle with the membranes in good condition. Any treatment of these organelles which disrupts membrane structure diminishes the ability to make ATP, although the electron transfer reactions themselves may be unimpaired. Attempts to prepare soluble phosphorylating preparations appear to have been quite unsuccessful. Mitchell suggests that the inability of workers to isolate the high-energy intermediates of ATP synthesis may be because

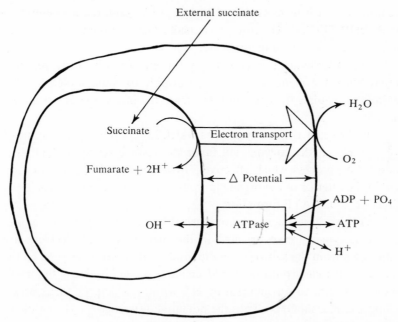

Figure 8–9. *Synthesis of ATP coupled to a potential difference across a membrane, as envisioned by Mitchell (see Suggested Reading). According to this hypothesis, the enzymes of electron transport are so situated in the membrane that electron flow occurs in an outward direction, thereby generating a potential and H^+ gradient. That gradient could drive an ATPase (ATP-splitting enzyme) in the direction of ATP synthesis provided that it is located in the membrane in such a way as to be inaccessible to water and accessible to OH^- from the inside and to H^+, ADP, PO_4, and ATP from the outside. ATP hydrolysis would require that OH^- approach from the inside and H^+ from the outside. The establishment of the potential difference (with a high internal H^+ concentration) would have the effect of removing OH^- from the inside and therefore would draw the reaction in the direction of ATP synthesis.*

they do not exist, and that the synthesis is in reality performed by a membrane-linked ATPase and driven by a sort of ion transport.

This view of ATP synthesis, which is called by Mitchell *chemiosmotic coupling*, is summarized in its simplest form in Figure 8–9. It depends on several postulates, all consistent with present knowledge of energy metabolism:

1. There is an ATP-hydrolyzing enzyme so situated in the organelle membrane that it is accessible to hydroxyl ion from the inside and to ATP, ADP, PO_4, and H^+ from the outside. The membrane is permeable to water, as such, from neither side.

2. The ATP-hydrolysis activity of the enzyme obviously requires water. Since the membrane is not permeable to water molecules, the hydrolysis requires the entry of OH^- from the inside and H^+ from the outside.

3. On the other hand, any process which lowers the concentration of $H^+ + OH^-$ at the enzyme will favor the reverse reaction, ATP synthesis. Any process which effectively lowered the OH^- concentration within the interior of the organelle would thus tend to pull things in the direction of net ATP formation.

4. ATP synthesis may be accomplished because the cytochromes and related enzymes are so oriented in the membrane that electrons are withdrawn from the substrate on the inside and passed to oxygen on the outside. Such electron flow would create a potential across the membrane and lead to an increase in H^+ within, which, in turn, would neutralize internal OH^-. Thus the potential difference (or H^+ gradient) due to electron transport would lead to ATP formation by the asymmetrically situated ATPase.

Without considering the theory in much greater detail, it is possible to note that none of the postulates are inconsistent with what is known about mitochondrial and chloroplast membranes, and also that the theory explains as much of what is known about the properties of ATP synthesis as does the purely chemical theory. To give one example, the chemical theory states that the action of an uncoupling agent such as dinitrophenol is to effect the hydrolysis of a high-energy intermediate, whereas the chemiosmotic view is that it serves as a hydrogen ion carrier within the membrane. In the latter case, the uncoupler, being dissolved in the membrane lipid, carries H^+ through the membrane and prevents any potential or H^+ gradient from being formed as a result of electron transport. This suggests that uncoupling agents should both be able to carry protons (H^+) and that they should be lipid-soluble, in order to have mobility in the membrane lipid. Examination of a number of compounds which uncouple oxidative and photosynthetic phosphorylation suggests that these two conditions are generally met. On the other hand, such examination does not necessarily produce a clear idea as to why uncouplers lead to the hydrolysis of intermediates of ATP synthesis, as required by the chemical theory, although our lack of knowledge as to the chemical nature of such intermediates would tend to make conclusions somewhat difficult.

An additional consequence of the chemiosmotic coupling hypothesis is that the orientation of the cytochrome system in the organelle membrane could also lead to a coherent explanation of active transport without recourse to chemical high-energy intermediates. Transport, especially of ions, could be driven by the electrochemical gradient set up by the electron transport associated with respiration. It is possible to envision ways for the gradient to be collapsed by the passage of ions across the membrane analogous to its collapse by the passage of hydrogen ion. Electron transport would tend to set up the gradient, and ion transport would tend to lower it, producing the observed effect of respiration driving ion translocation.

A great deal more might be said in support of the chemiosmotic view (the reader is referred to Mitchell's paper listed in Suggested Reading). On the other hand, available information does not permit one to choose between chemical and osmotic intermediates at the present time and the possibility is strong that the reality of ATP synthesis is more complex than either view alone. One bit of experimental evidence that does indicate that a proton gradient might drive ATP formation under some circumstances is the demonstration that isolated chloroplasts, in the dark, are able to synthesize some ATP in response to an abrupt change in the external pH, leading to a temporary gradient across the membrane. Since it is presently impossible to make a final decision about the chemiosmotic view, the theory is brought up in such length here, not as a statement of the way things are, but as a reminder that the answers about central matters in cell biology are by no means all at hand. Furthermore, the chemiosmotic theory serves as a reminder that membranes are very much directed (vectorial) units, and that transport and respiration are extremely intimately connected, both of which ideas the theory has brought before cell biologists with startling clarity.

Cell compartmentation and regulation

In Chapter 1 it was clear that cells are divided into a number of compartments by their internal membranes, whereas in this chapter it has been seen that the same membranes have considerable specificity as to the passage of chemicals. This suggests that compartmentation could play a significant role in the regulation of cell activity since the passage of molecules and ions between different parts of the cell could be strictly regulated. Furthermore, much translocation across membranes is dependent on energy production by the cell, so that energy metabolism, which is itself under tight control, influences transport in a fundamental way.

Experimentally, the question of compartmentation often arises when it is discovered that a cell organelle is not equally permeable to all materials or when a chemical compound appears to exist in distinct populations within the cell, with barriers to mixing between them. Similarly, changes in the reactivity of cells on disruption of structure often point to the existence of compartments, the barriers between which prevent the free reaction of the product of one enzymic reaction with another enzyme.

For example, the important compound, oxaloacetate, appears to exist in two compartments within mitochondria, being able to produce inhibition of succinate oxidation (see Chapter 5) only while in one of them. Other cases exist where a reaction occurs only when ATP is available, in situations which suggest that the role of ATP is to allow active transport to eliminate a membrane-imposed barrier to the complete reaction. Many cases of apparent compartmentization in cells may be cited, but instead we shall consider one central one in some detail—barriers to the free migration of pyridine nucleotides.

We have seen that an important aspect of the role of pyridine nucleotides (NAD^+ and $NADP^+$) in respiration is their ability to move about and thus serve as mobile electron carriers. We have seen, for example, that the acceptance of electrons in glycolysis may be coupled to the donation of them in the aerobic oxidation of NADH by the respiratory chain. This requires, at first sight, that NADH should be able to pass from the soluble cytoplasm, where the glycolytic enzymes are located, to the mitochondrion, where the oxidation by molecular oxygen occurs. A possible alternative would be the aerobic oxidation of

NADH by enzymes situated in the extramitochondrial cytoplasm, but such reactions do not, in fact, appear to occur. It is therefore interesting to learn that isolated, intact mitochondria are quite without the ability to oxidize external NADH but that the oxidation occurs rapidly when mitochondria are damaged.

It is clear, on the other hand, that mitochondria oxidize internal NADH, since it is formed in the course of oxidation of a number of substrates whose oxidation is NAD-linked and which pass freely through the mitochondrial membrane. Thus it is necessary to search for a mechanism which will explain the known role of NADH in mediating electron transfer between the reactions of glycolysis and the respiratory chain. Similar problems exist with respect to the role of NADPH, but one might suppose that the two difficulties are related, since a mechanism allowing NADH to ignore the barrier, together with the transhydrogenase reaction described earlier, would settle things for NADPH as well.

Transcompartment substrate cycles

It is clear that the mitochondrial barrier to NADH entry may not be avoided by any sort of special NADH transport mechanism, since the transport has been impossible to observe in undamaged mitochondria. Therefore, the passage of electrons from the extramitochondrial to the intramitochondrial compartment should be thought of as the transfer of electrons from outer to inner pyridine nucleotides (the reduction of internal NAD^+ by external NADH). Clearly, something must cross the mitochondrial membrane and, since isolated mitochondria do not oxidize NADH, it is likely to involve some component of cytoplasm which may be lost during the isolation procedure for mitochondria.

A method whereby electrons may be passed from external to mitochondrial pyridine nucleotides has been described and is called the *glycerol phosphate cycle*, summarized in Figure 8–10. The cycle depends on the presence of two enzymes for the oxidation of glycerol phosphate, a mitochondrial one, which is a flavoprotein passing electrons to oxygen via the cytochrome system, and an extramitochondrial pathway, where the electron acceptor is NAD^+. External NADH first reduces dihydroxyacetone-phosphate. The product of this reaction is NAD^+ and glycerol phosphate. The mitochondrial membrane is permeable to glycerol phosphate, which enters the mitochondrion and is there reoxidized by

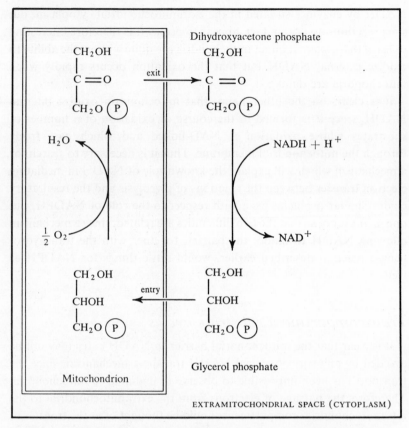

Figure 8–10. *Oxidation of NADH by the glycerol phosphate cycle.*

the respiratory chain to form di-hydroxyacetone-phosphate, which is free to diffuse to the outside and react again with NADH. The two reactions may be written in such a way that they add up to the net oxidation of NADH by mitochondria:

Extramitochondrial
$$NADH + H^+ + \text{dihydroxyacetone-PO}_4 \longrightarrow$$
$$NAD^+ + \text{glycerol-PO}_4$$

Mitochondrial
$$\text{Glycerol-PO}_4 + \tfrac{1}{2}O_2 \longrightarrow$$
$$\text{dihydroxyacetone-PO}_4 + H_2O$$

Sum: $NADH + \tfrac{1}{2}O_2 + H^+ \longrightarrow NAD^+ + H_2O$

It is probable that this mechanism accounts for a large part of NADH oxidation in mitochondria from a number of tissues. Additional cycles of a similar nature have been suggested using other NAD$^+$-linked substrates, but in all cases positive evidence is meager.

Finally, it is worth remarking that the glycerol phosphate cycle is itself subject to regulation in the cell insofar as it requires the presence of one of the intermediates of glycolysis for activity. This ensures that, under conditions where glycolysis is not continuously providing for the cytoplasmic reduction of NAD$^+$, mitochondrial oxidation of NADH will not occur, an arrangement which tends to conserve any NADH in the extramitochondrial space when its rate of production is low.

Suggested Reading

BIOCHEMICAL SOCIETY SYMPOSIUM, No. 16, "*The Structure and Function of Subcellular Components*," Cambridge University Press, Cambridge, 1959.

CHRISTENSEN, H. N., *Biological Transport*, W. A. Benjamin, New York, 1962.

HARRIS, E. J., *Transport and Accumulation in Biological Systems*, Butterworth & Co., London, 1956.

JOHNSON, F. H., H. EYRING, and M. J. POLISSAR, *The Kinetic Basis of Molecular Biology*, John Wiley & Sons, New York, 1954, Chap. 11.

LEHNINGER, A. L., *The Mitochondrion*, W. A. Benjamin, New York, 1964, Chaps. 7 and 8.

MITCHELL, P., "Chemiosmotic coupling in oxidative and photosynthetic phosphorylation," *Biol. Rev.*, **41**, 445 (1966).

SIEKEVITZ, P., "On the meaning of intracellular structure for metabolic regulation," in *CIBA Foundation Symposium, Regulation of Cell Metabolism*, G. E. W. Wolstenholme, and C. M. O'Connor (eds.), Little, Brown and Co., Boston, 1959.

CHAPTER 9

Physical Activities of Cells

A central feature of living matter is irritability, by which is meant the characteristic ability of living things to respond to a stimulus from without. A generalized sort of irritable response might be the generation of a change in surface potential when the immediate environment of a cell is perturbed. The contraction of a muscle fiber on electrical stimulation provides an additional example, as does an avoidance phenomenon elicited in single-celled organisms by light. In all cases cells make an extremely rapid response (of the order of milliseconds) to a stimulus which is not necessarily of the same sort as the response. In other words, a physical perturbation may elicit an electrical reaction and vice versa. The reader will recall that a number of categories of response to the environment have been discussed already, including, to name just one example, the synthesis of an induced enzyme upon the presentation of an inducing agent to a cell. Probably all such responses should be regarded as cases of irritability, although the term is usually used to refer to those with a relatively short time of completion.

Generation of potential at the cell surface

We saw in Chapter 8 that cellular membranes are able to translocate ions against a concentration gradient and so set up a potential difference between inside and outside. This ability is found in both the membranes of intracellular organelles and that surrounding the cell itself, where it is possible to measure the electrochemical potential difference between the surfaces of the membrane with microelectrodes. Thus cells are able to maintain a potential difference of about 50 mV across their membrane by the continuous maintenance of an ion gradient coupled to utilization of metabolic energy. A chemical that interferes with energy transfer in cells (such as an uncoupling agent) will lead to cessation of ion pumping and an elimination of the potential. The reader will recall that, according to the chemiosmotic hypothesis presented in Chapter 8, this observation cuts both ways, since an uncoupler is said to eliminate energy conservation *because* it is able to collapse the potential difference across membranes.

Owing to the performance of metabolic work, the cell is able to maintain a constant "resting" potential over its entire surface. If a portion of the surface is stimulated in such a way as to collapse the potential, a wave of such depolarization is seen to travel over the cell,

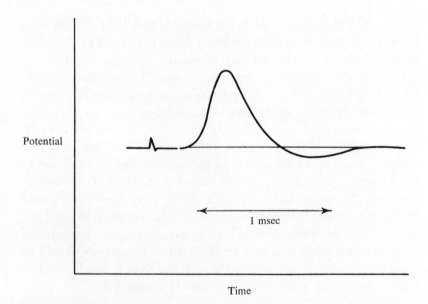

Figure 9–1. *Oscillographic record of an action potential traversing a frog sciatic nerve. Recording electrodes were placed 7 mm apart on the nerve. The small spike on the left of the trace is an artifact due to the electrical stimulus that was used to initiate the action potential.*

radiating away from the original site. Such a wave of potential decline is called an *action potential* (Figure 9–1) and forms the basis for the conduction of impulses by nerve cells and the consequent transmission of information between parts of multicellular organisms.

Nerve cells are especially good places to look for effects related to the action potential, because they are modified to permit the communication of potential differences through considerable distances. One may torment a nerve fiber and look for an effect at a point quite far removed from the site of torment, a great advantage if one is interested in the rate of travel of the impulse. The velocity in a variety of nerve cells from higher organisms turns out to about 25 meters per second. Nerve cells (neurons) are modified for this sort of information transfer, inasmuch as they are well-endowed with ATP hydrolysis-coupled ion pumping systems to enable rapid recovery of a potential gradient after a wave of collapse has passed by.

The ions involved in the formation of a cellular membrane potential gradient are potassium and chloride. Potassium exists in higher concentration within cells than in the extracellular fluid, which leads to a potential difference. The role of potassium in polarization of cell membranes is apparent from the observation that an artificial equalization of K^+ on both sides of the membrane leads to a disappearance of the resting membrane potential. It also appears that the partition of Cl^- across membranes is able to contribute to the total potential difference. It should be clear that the establishment of such a gradient by the distribution of K^+ and Cl^- would be impossible if there were other ions freely able to pass across the membrane. For example, the free migration of Na^+ would lead to a discharge of any potential formed by the K^+ gradient. For a single ion to maintain a stable potential, the movement of all others present would have to be restricted. Something of this sort appears to be the case, since in nerve cells Na^+, present in the normal extracellular fluid, is extruded from the cell by an active process.

Since the resting potential of cell membranes is a matter of ionic distribution, it follows that the collapse of potential (action potential) is a matter of perturbation of ionic distribution. One can think of the propagation of an action potential as consisting of two events, the first being depolarization as the result of an abrupt change in permeability to the ions responsible for the resting potential. Whatever the nature of this change, it must take place extremely rapidly (in milliseconds) and must obviously lead to an abrupt change in the conductivity of the membrane. This is followed by a second event, the recovery of the original potential, by means of active ion translocation. The first event appears to involve the triggered release of potential across a membrane by means of physical processes within the membrane. The second is more a matter of metabolic processes leading to ion translocation and has been studied extensively with respect to energy source, heat production, and the effect of metabolic inhibitors.

The reader should not be left with the impression that action potential is a feature of nerve cells only. Indeed, it appears to be a property of the membranes of cells generally and has been studied extensively, to cite just two cases, in heart muscle (electrocardiogram) and in cells of the freshwater alga Nitella.

Mechanical work by cells

The power of motion is a general property of living matter. Cells are able to move their parts and, often, themselves, by a variety of means, and thereby to perform mechanical work. The fact of irritability was described above, in terms of stimulus and response, and the response of a cell often involves motion. This is in keeping with the significant ability of many cells and aggregates of cells (multicellular organisms) to move in space in such manner as to minimize certain disadvantages connected with one particular region. This aspect of physiology is often included in the study of behavior and is exemplified by the movement of a cell away from a noxious stimulus or toward a relatively beneficent portion of space (one containing food). Such directed mechanical response is clearly of the greatest importance in considering the control of cell activities, and it must be said that relatively little is known about the details of its mechanism and, further, that experiments directed to such investigation have proved not at all easy to design.

Cell motion falls into two categories, motion of the whole cell and motion within the boundaries of a cell. The former takes place by means of flagella and cilia (short, numerous flagella) as well as by the little-understood process of gliding motility found in blue-green algae and Myxobacteria, where there is said to be direct contact between the cytoplasm and the environment. The muscle cells of complex organisms move as a unit by means of intracellular muscle filaments involving mechanisms to be described later.

On the other hand, intracellular motion includes such varied processes as protoplasmic streaming, events connected with mitosis, contraction of such organelles as mitochondria, and pinocytosis. It is well known that, in mitosis, chromosomes are drawn apart by contractile fibers associated with the spindle apparatus and that some form of mechanical work is associated with the separation of a dividing cell into its two progeny. The limiting membrane of cells is likewise capable of movement as seen in the active in-pocketing associated with the engulfment of external fluid (pinocytosis). Special organelles with the power of motion, often bearing a close relation to the cell membrane, include trichocysts and contractile vacuoles, found in protozoans. Mitochondria have been shown to undergo cycles of contraction and swelling related to events associated with energy transfer. A contractile protein rather like that of muscle has been isolated from mitochondria and is believed by some to provide the basis for mitochondrial contraction, although this is not universally accepted. Similar cycles of volume change have been observed in isolated chloroplasts.

The molecular basis for contraction

Most of what is known about contractile processes in cells has been discovered by the study of muscle. Although we shall follow this emphasis, it is well to note that many of the statements that may be made about muscle contraction are also valid for other systems, insofar as we know anything about them. Thus it should not be very surprising that mammalian muscle and bacterial flagella contain a contractile protein with properties in common, since Nature appears to follow similar routes at different times in evolution.

Muscle cells (see Figure 9–2) contain bands of protein, largely composed of two molecular species, actin and myosin, which provide the basis for contraction. Physical measurements indicate that myosin is an elongated molecule with a molecular weight of about 500,000 and a ratio of length to width estimated to be about 100. Furthermore, in the presence of calcium, myosin possesses enzymatic activity, ATPase, wherein it catalyzes the hydrolysis of ATP to ADP and inorganic phosphate. Since ATP hydrolysis appears to provide energy for muscular contraction, it seems necessary that some part of the contractile apparatus should exhibit ATPase activity.

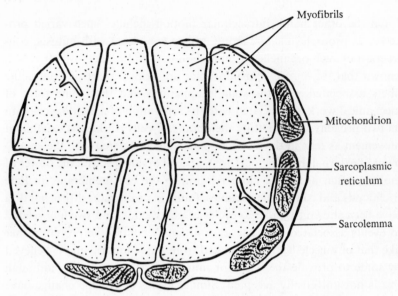

Figure 9–2.   *Diagram showing the organization of a muscle fiber in cross section. Note the mitochondria in close contact with the myofibrils and the sarcolemma (muscle cell membrane) continuous with the sarcoplasmic (endoplasmic) reticulum. A higher magnification (or a less diagrammatic view) would reveal the myofibrils to contain an array of filaments, also in cross section, which are identical to the actin and myosin strands shown in Figure 9–3.*

Indeed, the other important protein of muscle, actin, with a molecular weight of about 60,000, is also able to show ATPase activity under suitable conditions. It is interesting that actin exists as either a monomer or a polymer and that incubation of the monomer with ATP leads to its polymerization, coupled to ATP hydrolysis.

A third aspect of the ATPase activity of muscle protein is related to the formation of a complex between actin and myosin. It appears that in the intact cell actin and myosin exist in close association, sometimes being referred to as actomyosin. Careful extraction from muscle may lead to the purification of the intact complex, which may also be reconstituted from purified actin and myosin. The complex retains the ability to hydrolyze ATP, and in this case the hydrolysis leads to its dissociation into free actin and myosin. The relation between complex formation and contraction may be seen in Figure 9–3, where the probable geometry of the complex is diagrammed. It is probable that what is referred to as a

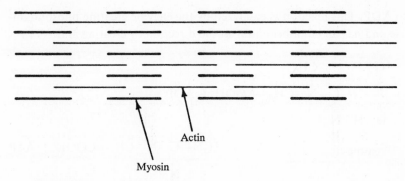

Figure 9–3. *Geometry of the actin-myosin complex in muscle.*

complex in the test tube is *in vivo* a matter of cross-bonding between the molecules of actin and myosin in the parallel array. Present thinking about muscular contraction is along the lines of a sliding arrangement, where the ATP-induced breaking of bonds between adjacent actin or myosin molecules leads to a lateral movement (as seen in the figure) driven by electrostatic forces.

The energy source for contraction

The discovery of ATPase activity in muscle protein might be expected to remove any ambiguity as to the source of energy for contraction. Quite on the contrary, the energy source for *in vivo* motion has proved somewhat elusive, with a number of molecules being suggested as possible candidates from time to time. In the first place, contraction may take place under either aerobic or anaerobic conditions. In the absence of oxygen, energy production proceeds by way of glycolysis, leading to the production of lactate. When glycolysis is blocked by an inhibitor such as iodoacetate, contraction can still take place, but with a loss of intracellular energy. Under such conditions, it is of obvious interest to see what molecules decline in concentration, as one would expect any "energy-rich" one to become exhausted.

Under such conditions of limited energy input and repeated contraction, one observes that the ATP content of muscle cells remains constant, while that of creatine phosphate declines. The reason for this turns out to be not a primary role for creatine phosphate in contraction but, rather, a reaction whereby creatine phosphate transfers phosphate to ADP. This reaction is catalyzed by the enzyme creatine phosphokinase and has an equilibrium far in the direction of creatine and ATP:

$$
\begin{array}{c}
\underset{\substack{\text{Creatine-}\textcircled{P}}}{
\overset{\displaystyle O}{\underset{\displaystyle O}{O\!-\!\underset{|}{\overset{|}{P}}\!-\!\underset{H}{\overset{|}{N}}\!-\!\underset{\underset{H}{N}}{\overset{CH_3}{\underset{|}{C}}}\!-\!N\!-\!CH_2\!-\!COOH}}
} + ADP \rightleftharpoons
\end{array}
$$

$$
H_2N\!-\!\underset{\underset{H}{\overset{||}{N}}}{\overset{\overset{CH_3}{|}}{C}}\!-\!N\!-\!CH_2\!-\!COOH + ATP
$$

Creatine

ATP is, in fact, the primary energy source for muscular contraction, but as soon as any is hydrolyzed under the catalysis of actomyosin, the thermodynamically favorable phosphate transfer takes place to maintain the ATP level in the cell. Evidence for the direct involvement of ATP comes from a number of circumstantial arguments, but primarily from the fact that, when creatine phosphokinase is inhibited by fluorodinitrobenzene, contraction is entirely at the expense of ATP hydrolysis. A role for ATP as a primary energy source is entirely consistent with its known major function in other energy-requiring processes, as well as the striking juxtaposition of mitochondria (sites of major ATP formation) to the contractile fibers of muscle cells (where it is used).

Other contractile processes

There appears to be a unity of mechanism for contractile events in cells where the remarks made above about muscle apply to the other contractile systems. The reason that most of our present knowledge about the area comes from studies with muscle stems largely from such practical matters as the medical implications of muscle physiology and the fact that muscle protein may be obtained in very large quantities, permitting a variety of experiments that would be quite impossible with the minute quantities of flagellar or spindle fiber protein found in a cell. It does appear, however, that in all cases studied the power of motion is associated with a protein, and, where it is possible to say anything about the physical characteristics of that protein, it looks rather similar to the actomyosin system. Thus the outer fibers of an eucaryotic flagellum or the entirety of a bacterial flagellum have many of the properties of acto-myosin, including ATPase activity.

Suggested Reading

DAVIES, R. E., "On the mechanism of muscular contraction," in *Essays in Biochemistry*, P. N. Campbell and G. D. Greville (eds.), Vol. 1, Academic Press, New York, 1965.

KATZ, B., *Nerves, Muscles and Synapses*, McGraw-Hill Book Co., New York, 1966.

LEHNINGER, A. L., *Bioenergetics*, W. A. Benjamin, New York, 1965, Chap. 8.

PERRY, S. V., "Muscular contraction," in *Comparative Biochemistry*, M. Florkin and H. S. Mason (eds.), Academic Press, New York, 1960.

CHAPTER 10

Cell Growth

Cell growth is the manufacture of cells by cells and represents a summation of all the biosynthetic and energy-capturing reactions discussed thus far. Any control that is exerted on the reactions that comprise growth may be expected to influence the growth rate itself. Similarly, normal growth is unlikely to be maintained under conditions where important phases of synthesis or energy conversion are interfered with. Cell growth is often thought of as identical to cell division, although, in fact, the two are quite distinct. For example, a cell population can be shown to grow (increase in mass) under various conditions without cell division taking place. Furthermore, all our measurements of growth can be shown to be quite unrelated to the manner in which cells divide. Thus if cells divided into thirds instead of halves, the growth rate as well as our methods of describing it would be unaltered.

Growth rates of cell populations

An accurate description of growth will be seen to involve a certain amount of mathematics which, however, only reflects an extremely simple feature of growth, the fact that cell material is its own factory. This may be expressed in a number of ways, including the statement that cells are

175

autocatalytic (they make cells), but, most significantly, this implies that the rate of increase in cell material is proportional to the amount of cell material present to begin with. In other words, if one has twice the cell material, one observes twice the rate of increase in cell material, because twice the number of factories turn it out.

Now, it is possible to speak of the "amount" of cell material, but, to be a little more specific about units, it is useful to see how growth might actually be measured and represented. The units commonly used in studies of cell growth include the number of cells and the mass of cell material. The two may be interconverted readily as long as the average mass of a cell in a population remains constant, and this is generally the case, except under certain conditions to be described later. Expression of the mass of a population of cells growing in suspension might well be expressed in terms of milligrams per milliliter.

Actual measurement of the number of cells in a population includes such techniques as visual counting of cells in the known volume of a cytometer chamber, photometric measurement of the light scattering by a turbid suspension of cells, and finally by what is called a *viable cell count*. The latter, which is usually applied to bacterial populations, involves plating known volumes of known dilutions of the original sample evenly on solid medium in a Petri dish, and counting the colonies formed. One assumes that each colony originated with a single cell, and this assumption is sufficiently true to allow the method to be used extensively. In contrast with other techniques, the viable cell count gives only the number of cells which are in good enough condition to divide and give rise to colonies, so that results may be lower than cell counts by optical methods.

In the following discussion we shall ignore the method by which cell growth is followed and shall use cell number and cell mass interchangeably, denoting both as N. First, let us consider a population of cells growing in liquid culture. These might be any sort of cell, including bacterial or mammalian, and our only requirements are that there be no unusual conditions influencing growth and that there be a constant volume. Since we found that the rate of growth of a population of cells was proportional to the amount present to begin with, we can say that

Growth rate $= k$ (the amount of cells)

where k is a proportionality constant. This may be written more simply as

$$\frac{dN}{dt} = k(N) \qquad \text{(Eq. 1)}$$

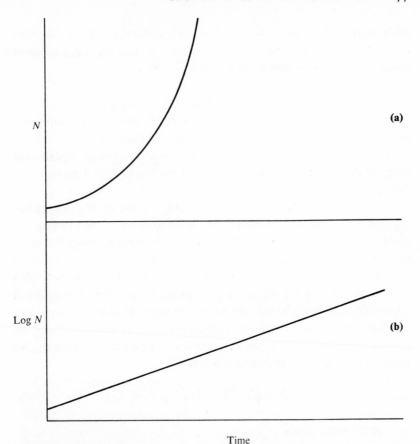

Figure 10–1. *Exponential growth. (a) The number (or mass) of cells (N) is expressed directly as a function of time. (b) The log of N is plotted against a linear time axis (semilogarithmic graph).*

where dN/dt is the rate of change of the amount of cells, N, with respect to time—the growth rate. This equation may be rearranged to give

$$\frac{dN}{N} = k \, dt$$

This may be integrated

$$\int \frac{dN}{N} = k \int dt$$

which gives*

$$\log_e N = kt + C \qquad\qquad\qquad \text{(Eq. 2)}$$

---

* If this step is not clear, the reader may either look it up in a table of integrals or accept it on faith.

where C is an integration constant and the logarithm is taken to the base $e = 2.718\ldots$. It must be said that the base of the log is not of great importance in this equation, since the constant may be adjusted to take care of different bases. Indeed logs to the base 10 or 2 are commonly used in growth studies. Equation 2 may be expressed as the log of the number of cells being proportional to time. The constant C simply sets the base line for the increase and can be moved about. If equation 2 is a valid representation of growth (which it is), one could predict that plotting the log of N versus time would give rise to a straight line, and this is seen in Figure 10–1(b) to be the case.

As valid as Equation 2 is, the arbitrary nature of the integration constant C may bother the reader, and actually there is a way to be more precise. It is possible to eliminate C by considering the integration to be carried out within certain limits, to be determined by practical aspects of a growth experiment. Let us choose to consider only a portion of a growth curve (Figure 10–2) in a region of the curve where measurement is convenient. Let N_0 be the amount of cell material when $t = 0$ (t_0) and consider the amount to have increased to N_1 at time t_1. Then the integration shown above may be carried out within these limits to give the actual increase of N during the interval:

$$\int_{N_0}^{N_1} \frac{dN}{N} = k \int_{t_0}^{t_1} dt$$

This integration yields

$$\log_e N_1 - \log_e N_0 = k(t_1 - t_0)$$

or, since $t = 0$ at t_0,

$$\log_e N_1 - \log_e N_0 = kt_1$$

This may be written

$$\log_e \frac{N_1}{N_0} = kt_1 \qquad \text{(Eq. 3)}$$

or, raising both sides of the equation to the base e,

$$\frac{N_1}{N_0} = e^{kt_1} \qquad \text{(Eq. 4)}$$

Thus we have obtained an exponential equation for the growth of a cell population (Equation 4), and it may be written in the completely equivalent logarithmic form of Equation 3. These equations represent nothing more than the mathematical consequence of the previously mentioned fact that cell (and all) growth has an autocatalytic character.

It should be recognized that these equations are of considerable generality in the natural world, since a number of inanimate processes also exhibit kinetic properties that are exponential. For example, these relations hold rigorously for the process of radioactive decay as long as there is a change in the sign. This is due to the obvious fact that, as decay occurs, the amount of the material decaying diminishes, so there is less material left to decay.

The doubling time

The reader is, no doubt, familiar with the idea of the half-life of a radioactive isotope as a characteristic feature of a given isotope. A similar quantity may be defined in the case of growth, which, since the polarity of growth and decay are opposite, is termed the *doubling time*.

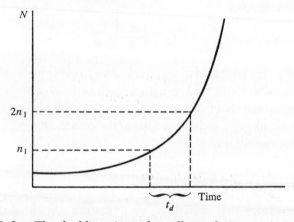

Figure 10–2. *The doubling time of a cell population. n_1 is an arbitrary measure of the size of the population, t_d the time required for it to reach $2n_1$. Note that t_d is independent of the point originally selected for n_1.*

It is written t_d and is the time required for a population of cells to double in weight or number. While the actual growth rate is dependent on the number of cells present, the doubling time is not, and is a characteristic of a given type of cell under given conditions of environment. The reader should satisfy himself as to the truth of this last remark by careful examination of the growth equations, perhaps working out a specific example. It is possible to derive an expression for t_d from Equation 3. Since

$$\log_e N_1 = \log_e N_0 + kt_1$$

and since, at the end of the doubling time

$$N_1 = 2N_0$$

and

$$t = t_d$$

we may write

$$\log_e(2N_0) = \log_e N_0 + kt_d$$

from which

$$\log_e N_0 + \log_e 2 = \log_e N_0 + kt_d$$

or

$$\log_e 2 = kt_d$$

Finally, solving for t_d,

$$t_d = \frac{\log_e 2}{k} \qquad \text{(Eq. 5)}$$

This is really very useful, since $\log_e 2$ is known to many places (0.693...). Thus it is possible to obtain k, usually known as the *growth rate constant*, from information about the doubling time. It is clear that the growth rate constant, like t_d, is a characteristic of the growth of a given organism under given conditions.

Limitation of the growth rate

The knowledge that growth is, by its nature, exponential leads to some conclusions about the range of validity of the treatment above. Clearly, if a pair of cells divide, and their progeny divide one doubling time later, and so on, then their numbers describe an exponential progression of the form 2, 4, 8, 16, 32, 64,.... Since a given cell would have a life span much longer than the doubling time, and since the exponential nature of growth brings one to very large numbers very quickly after a finite number of generations, one should expect the progeny of a given cell literally to take over the world. It has been calculated that the mass of a population of *Escherichia coli* originating from one cell dividing every 30 minutes would in a few days come to equal that of the solar system. That is, however, at least one catastrophe that does not seem to occur. In other words, something intervenes to limit the infinite expansion of populations, and the exponential character of growth is maintained only for a portion of the life span of a population. It is of considerable interest to see how a population of cells really behaves and to discover the reasons for the fact that growth does not proceed to infinite excesses.

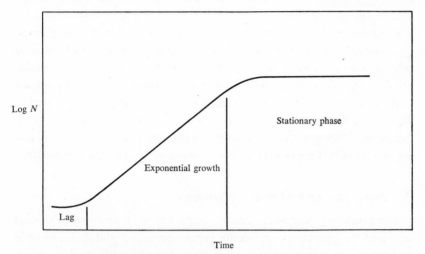

Figure 10–3.   *Growth of a cell population.*

Figure 10–3 shows the idealized growth of a population of cells growing in a constant volume. We imagine that, at $t = 0$, cells are placed in a new medium and allowed to grow. One observes first a period when growth does not commence; this is termed the *lag period*. The lag period may be described simply as the time required for the cells to adjust their internal chemistry to the tasks of utilizing a new medium, which is probably in part a question of the synthesis of new induced enzymes appropriate to the nutrients available. As one might predict, when cells that have been growing actively are placed in a medium of a composition similar to that in which they have been residing, the lag period is diminished or missing altogether.

Following the lag period, the cells begin to grow at an increasing rate until growth becomes truly exponential. During the exponential phase of growth, the population may be described in terms of the equations presented earlier. It is, however, of finite duration, and the population passes through a declining growth rate until the stationary phase is reached, where net growth has ceased. The decline in growth is due to the exhaustion of nutrients in the medium as well as to the formation of toxic products of cell metabolism. Thus the addition of nutrients that are limiting will give rise to additional growth, as will the removal of waste products from the medium. In many instances it appears that the stationary phase represents a sort of equilibrium where there is some growth, balanced with and dependent on the dissolution of some of the cells of the population.

It is important to realize that the term *growth medium* should be used in a context wide enough to include not only the medium of cultured cells (*in vitro*) but also the medium formed by the totality of a multi-cellular organism. It is clear that cells growing in such a complex medium experience many of the same limitations on growth, related to nutrition and to the removal of wastes, as do isolated cells. Such "ecological" considerations are of the greatest importance in relating the results of cell physiology to the function of multicellular organisms.

Systems for continuous growth

The preceding comments about the growth of a real population of cells and the limitations to infinite expansion of a population are valid as long as the cells exist in a constant volume of medium with no re-plenishment of nutrients or removal of toxic products. It is possible to devise a situation where these restrictions are avoided and where growth may be maintained in the exponential phase for extended periods of time.

Such a device for the continuous cultivation of cells is known as a *chemostat* and depends upon the continuous addition of new medium to a population of cells growing in a container. The addition of medium at once provides new nutrients and leads to the dilution of waste products and cells, so there is no reason why a declining phase of growth should be observed. The addition of medium is at a rate such that the formation of new cells by cell division is exactly balanced by the dilution of cells, so that, although the population grows exponentially, the total number and mass of cells per unit volume remains constant. Apparatus of this sort has proved of great value in studying the growth of cells from a variety of taxonomic groups, although bacterial growth has been most extensively examined. It might be argued that the continuous flow situation of the chemostat is somewhat artificial and that results obtained in this way are not likely to be of great relevance to the study of cells under conditions normal for them. In fact, the steady-state condition achieved in a flow system is in some ways not unlike that of the organism as a whole, and the possibility of looking at cells under conditions not changing with time represents a unique opportunity in the investigation of growth and metabolic events related to it.

One of the advantages in studying growth under conditions of continuous flow is the precise measurement of growth rate, dN/dt, the growth rate constant, k, and the doubling time t_d that becomes possible. To see how this occurs, one must consider the design of such a system, outlined in Figure 10–4. Sterile medium drops, or is pumped, at a controlled rate into the growth tube. As medium is added, an equal volume

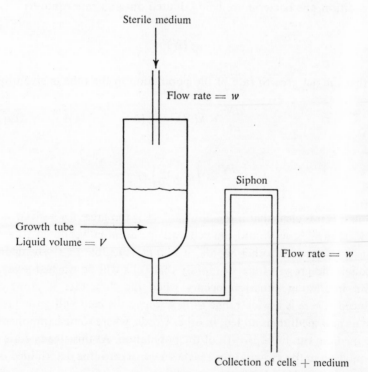

Figure 10–4. *Diagram of a chemostat. Additional details, not shown, include devices for maintaining a constant flow rate and temperature as well as provisions for aeration.*

of medium and cells is siphoned off and may be collected. Thus, owing to the action of the siphon, the volume in the growth tube remains constant, and a steady state is possible, where the cell density remains constant with time. The quantitative usefulness of the system stems from the constant volume and the equality between the rate of dilution of cells and that of new cell formation. Then let V be the volume of the growth tube in milliliters and w be the flow rate through the whole system in milliliters per hour. Obviously both numbers may be obtained with great accuracy, the latter by simply holding a graduated cylinder under the siphon for an hour. We know that the bacteria are growing inside the tube at a rate determined by the equation

$$\frac{dN}{dt} = k(N) \qquad \text{(Eq. 1)}$$

In addition, the bacteria are being diluted out at a rate equal to

$$\frac{w}{V}(N)$$

so that the net growth rate of the population in the tube is given by

$$\frac{dN}{dt} = k(N) - \frac{w}{V}(N) \qquad \text{(Eq. 6)}$$

or

$$\frac{dN}{dt} = \left(k - \frac{w}{V}\right)(N)$$

From this it is clear that if the flow rate, w, is too great for a given value of V, then $K \ll w/V$, and the cells will be eventually diluted to a cell density of zero. In other words, it is quite possible to slosh medium through the growth tube so rapidly that cells will be washed away. A more interesting situation occurs when the flow rate is somewhat reduced. There is a wide range of flow where the cells will grow just as fast as new medium is added, in other words, where some component of the medium can limit growth of the population. At this steady state the population in the growth tube reaches a constant value determined only by the rate of flow. Under this condition

$$\frac{dN}{dt} = \left(k - \frac{w}{V}\right)(N) = 0$$

and it is clear that

$$k = \frac{w}{V} \qquad \text{(Eq. 8)}$$

From k it is possible to determine the doubling time t_d, as described above.

Thus we find a third means of determining the growth rate constant k the first two being via Equations 1 and 5. We said that k was a property of a population under a given set of conditions, and this is demonstrated clearly by our ability to change k, within a certain range, by simply altering the rate of flow.

Continuous flow systems, however, are good for quite a bit more than determining growth constants, and variations have been built that perform many wonders, including the constant monitoring of cell pH and density so that a feedback link with the flow-rate control can maintain the cells at constant conditions. It should be emphasized that the culture of cells at a constant density, N, does not require any tricks other than a suitable flow rate and proper medium. The ability to change the growth rate of a cell population by simply changing a liquid flow rate is of great interest to those who wish to study the metabolic aspects of growth. It is especially interesting that, in the tube of the chemostat, the growth rate constant, k, and the cell density at the steady state, N, may be varied independently, N being related only to the nutrient content of the medium.

Synchronous growth

Increase in cell number is a quantum-like event, in that it takes place in a stepwise manner. There is no intermediate state between one and two cells. Thus one might expect a growth curve to look like a flight of stairs, with the population doubling each time the doubling time rolls around. This, of course, does not usually occur, because cells divide at random times within the population, so that cell division is spread over the whole doubling period. Even if we start out with one cell, by the time a few cell divisions have occurred the divisions are well spread out and the growth curve is smooth. This is a pity, because it would be very useful in the study of growth to be able to examine a population of cells, all about to divide. It is difficult to adduce metabolic features of cell division if the population is random with respect to it.

Fortunately, there are ways to synchronize cell division in a large population of cells so that things happen at the same time, at least for a while. These approaches, which have been applied principally to bacterial and protozoan studies, depend, with one exception, on interfering with the normal function of cells to such an extent that division is held in abeyance until conditions return to normal, at which time division takes place all at once in the population. For example, the withholding of an important cell constituent (such as thymine required for DNA synthesis) prevents cell division, and, when cells thus treated are returned to a thymine-containing medium, cell division occurs in synchrony. The first few divisions remain in step, but soon the time of division becomes increasingly random and the growth curve smooths out (see Figure 10–5). A similar experiment may be performed, not by starvation, but by

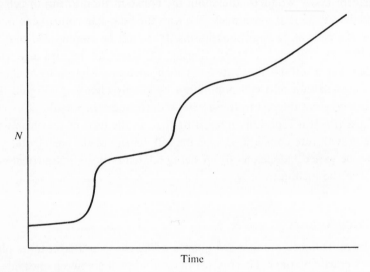

Figure 10–5. *Growth of a population whose cells initially divide in synchrony.*

raising the temperature of the cells about 10 degrees in a very short time. It is interesting that synchrony may also be produced by placing bacterial spores into suitable medium, after which germination and division take place initially in a coordinated fashion. This method is of limited applicability, since most cells do not form spores. Clearly, all methods described thus far for establishing synchrony of cell division depend on tormenting cells in a rather drastic way, hardly the way to examine "normal" cell division. The one technique that avoids this difficulty to a good measure depends on the rapid filtration of bacteria using calibrated filters to separate cells about to divide (the largest cells in the population) from those that have just divided (the smallest ones). Thus one is able to obtain a measure of synchrony without fiddling around with the physiology of the cells, and one may feel that the cells are in a somewhat more natural state.

It is important to note that the ability to synchronize the time of division of a population need not influence the over-all growth rate. Indeed, growth and division are two independent matters, and it is possible to arrange things so that growth occurs for a considerable period without cell division occurring at all. Similarly, it is possible to grow cells under such nutritional conditions that they are unable to make some important component such as DNA or RNA at a rate consistent with the growth of the cell as a whole. Thus, as the cells grow in a total mass, the protein content of the population may increase while the DNA/protein ratio may actually decline. Clearly, this situation cannot continue for very long and must lead to a decline in viability. However, while it lasts, it is known as *unbalanced growth* and provides some opportunities to study the role of various cell components on the growth process.

Metabolic aspects of growth

For a number of reasons, both practical and theoretical, the study of biochemical events related to growth has been vigorous, especially as might relate to the problem of the control of growth rate. When considering the results of investigations, it is important to make a clear distinction between aspects of growth and those of cell division. For example, there is a great deal of information, largely derived from synchronous growth studies, related to changes in the chemical composition of cells in different stages in their cycle of cell division and without reference to the rate of growth itself. One may observe a cyclic change in the percentage composition of cells with respect to protein, RNA, or DNA, with a period related to the time of division. At the present time such changes are somewhat difficult to interpret, as there is some question how much of the change is correlated with the cycle of division and how much with mistreatment of cells. Results differ, depending on the method used to induce synchrony.

Equally interesting are the results of studies on the relationship between cell composition and growth rate. By means of the chemostat it is possible to vary the growth rate continuously over a considerable range by adjusting the flow rate. Thus there is an infinity of possible rates of growth and, correspondingly, of possible cellular metabolic states. Thus it is of great interest to change the growth rate and to examine the cell composition on the grounds that any component uniquely associated with growth should bear a special relation to its rate.

When such experiments are performed using bacteria, a complication in the form of varying amounts of nuclear material per cell under different conditions interposes difficulties in the interpretation of results. In other words, it is possible to obtain conditions where unbalanced growth occurs to the extent that the bacterial nuclear material is replicated at a rate differing from that of cell division, and it is probable that the amount of a component should be expressed in terms of DNA, rather than on a per cell basis. If this is done, one observes that the protein/DNA ratio shows a slight correlation with growth rate, whereas the cell mass/DNA ratio is more significantly increased by an increase in growth. Most of the increase is accounted for by the increase in ribosomes as the growth rate goes up. Ribosomes (and ribosomal RNA) appear especially sensitive to the growth state of cells, and there appears to be an exponential relationship between them, on one hand, and the DNA, on the other. Since ribosomes are known to be the site of most cell protein synthesis, and since active growth must include active protein synthesis, it is not at all odd that the rate of protein formation is also correlated with growth rate. It seems clear that ribosomes exist in the cell under conditions of constant size and composition, so that the increase in total ribosomal material (or RNA) must be due to an increase in the number of ribosomes.

Thus the number of ribosomes in a cell appears dependent upon the growth rate of a population. It is extremely interesting to know if the growth rate is itself dependent upon the ribosome content (to consider if the causation might work both ways). Most of the evidence about this point comes from kinetic studies in which cells are shifted from one growth rate to another by alterations in temperature or medium and the changes in cell components noted. Suffice it to say that in such experiments RNA is always the first component to change, so that, when cells are jumped to a higher growth rate and rate of RNA formation increases as rapidly as it is possible to measure, the other components (DNA and protein), as well as total cell mass, begin to increase at the new rate only after the RNA level has approached a new steady state. Thus, although it is still impossible to say what component is responsible for the regulation of growth, or indeed if any one component can have such a role, it is clear that RNA is a likely candidate for at least a major influence.

Suggested Reading

GUNSALUS, I. C., and R. Y. STANIER, *The Bacteria*, Vol. IV, Academic Press, New York, 1962.

MAALØE, O., "The nucleic acids and the control of bacterial growth," in *Microbial Genetics*, W. Hayes and R. C. Clowes (eds.), Cambridge University Press, Cambridge, 1960.

MONOD, J., "The growth of bacterial cultures," *Ann. Rev. Microbiol*, **3**, 371 (1949).

NOVICK, A., "Growth of bacteria," *Ann. Rev. Microbiol*, **9**, 99 (1955).

CHAPTER 11

The Ultimate Control:
DNA and Protein Synthesis

In earlier chapters our examination of a number of aspects of the life of the cell led us to discuss selected examples of regulatory mechanisms. Of course, these examples represent a small fraction of those known. The proportion of known to unknown regulatory mechanisms could be compared to an iceberg, where the bulk is still undiscovered. Our concern in this chapter will be with the genetic forms of control that occur in cells, and we shall again be forced to adopt the tactic of considering only a small fraction of what is actually known. We shall begin by considering what is meant by genetic control (and therefore by the genetic code) and shall examine the operation and control of protein synthesis as an example of "reading out" that code.

Genetics studies the continuity between generations of cells and attempts to discover mechanisms behind it. The central element to all modern genetic theory is that there is a master plan (genotype) that somehow determines the observed properties (phenotype) of organisms. In this age of information theory, the genotype is often referred to as the *genetic code* and is believed to reside, in many cases, with a single molecular species, deoxyribonucleic acid (DNA). Whether the *totality* of the genetic code resides in DNA or whether it represents one among several forms of information storage is an important question at the present time and will be discussed in the last section.

Why DNA is probably genetic material

At a time in the 1930s when the essential chemistry of proteins and and their role as enzymes were becoming understood, nucleic acids represented something of an enigma in cell chemistry. They had been known as cell components for about a century, but their function was completely obscure. Then, over a period of about a decade, a series of observations was made which, together, indicated that the nucleic acids play a central part in the genetic regulation of cell activities. For one thing, it appeared from histochemical studies that DNA was located in the nucleus and specifically concentrated in the chromatin material, already known to involve mechanisms of genetic control. Furthermore, it developed that there was, in a given organism, a constant amount of DNA per nucleus and that diploid and haploid cells differed by a factor of 2 in this regard. Since diploid cells contain twice the number of genes found in the haploid state, this provided an additional suggestion that DNA had something to do with heredity. However, all evidence remained somewhat circumstantial until a single experiment was performed, which at once indicated clearly that DNA was the chemical entity in which genetic information was somehow encoded.

Seldom is a single experimental approach a turning point in science, but the discovery of bacterial transformation in 1944 by Avery, McLeod, and McCarty was such an instance. Their experiment made use of two strains of *Diplococcus pneumoniae*, which differed in the ability to make a functional capsule external to the cell wall. They showed that DNA, isolated from capsule-producing cells, when added to a culture of non-capsule cells, gave that population the ability to produce capsule. In other words, the information required to manufacture capsule was transferred from one population to another in the form of chemically pure DNA. In addition, it was observed that the enzyme deoxyribo-nuclease (DNAase), which specifically hydrolyzes DNA, completely destroyed the transforming ability. Additional transformation experiments were performed using a variety of other bacteria and resulting in the transfer of a number of genetic traits. Clearly DNA is able to encode a variety of genetic information.

Structure of nucleic acids

The demonstration of genetic information being carried by a chemical compound (DNA) at once leads to questions about the structure of the compound and the nature of the code. Hopefully, answers to either one of the questions should shed light on the other.

Nucleic acids are polymers which, on hydrolysis, yield 5-carbon sugars, nucleotide bases, and phosphate. Structures of these components are shown in Figure 11–1. Furthermore, there is a general pattern according to which the components are put together, whether in DNA or RNA,

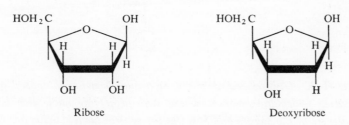

Figure 11–1. *Components of nucleic acids.*

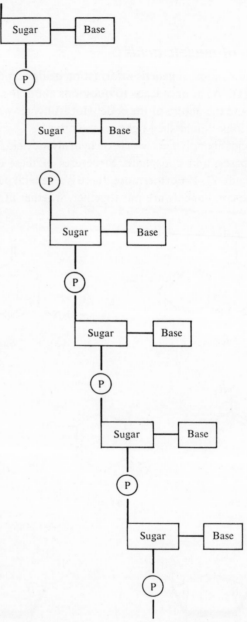

Figure 11–2. *Generalized structure of a nucleic acid, composed of an alternating phosphate-sugar backbone with projecting nucleotide bases. The identity of the sugars and bases in the several nucleic acids are given in Table* 11–1.

and this basic structure is shown in Figure 11–2. The polymer may thus be viewed as consisting of a homogeneous repeating backbone composed of sugar and phosphate, to which is attached a series of nucleotide bases which may differ from each other. The appropriateness of nucleic acids to the task of bearing information about heredity resides in the nucleotide bases projecting from the backbone, which may be thought of as letters of the code that determines cell properties.

There are important differences between DNA and RNA, as well as between the various types of RNA, which play roles in the cell to be discussed later. These properties are summarized in Table 11–1, where it is shown that DNA may be either single- or double-stranded, although the double-stranded form appears universal in all systems with the exception of viruses. All DNA contains deoxyribose as its major sugar component and all of it contains thymine, whereas RNA contains uracil.

TABLE 11–1
PROPERTIES OF NUCLEIC ACIDS

Species	Sugar	Bases	No. of bases [Approx.]	Location
DNA (double-stranded)	deoxyribose	adenine, guanine, cytosine, thymine	10^8	all cells
DNA (single-stranded)				some bacterial viruses
Transfer RNA	ribose	adenine, guanine, cytosine, uracil	10^2	cytoplasm
Messenger RNA			10^3	nucleus-cytoplasm
Ribosomal RNA			10^6	ribosomes

Some of the most significant features of the structures of the several nucleic acids concern their three-dimensional configuration in space, which is a consequence of their composition. In the cases of RNA and single-stranded DNA, the molecules are in the form of a single chain with some regions of helical structure. In these instances the conformation is determined by hydrogen bonds between the various bases. In the case of double-stranded DNA, hydrogen bonds also play an important role in determining three-dimensional structure, which takes the form of the twin-stranded helix, probably now familiar to all students of biology.

The symmetry of the DNA helix, as well as its central function in cell biology, comes from the interaction between nucleotide bases in the paired strands. Not only do the bases maintain positions with relation to each other by means of hydrogen bonding, but there is a very interesting specificity to such pairing. For geometric reasons the bases are able to form hydrogen bonds only between the pairs *thymine-adenine* and *cytosine-guanine*. Figure 11–3 illustrates the basis for such

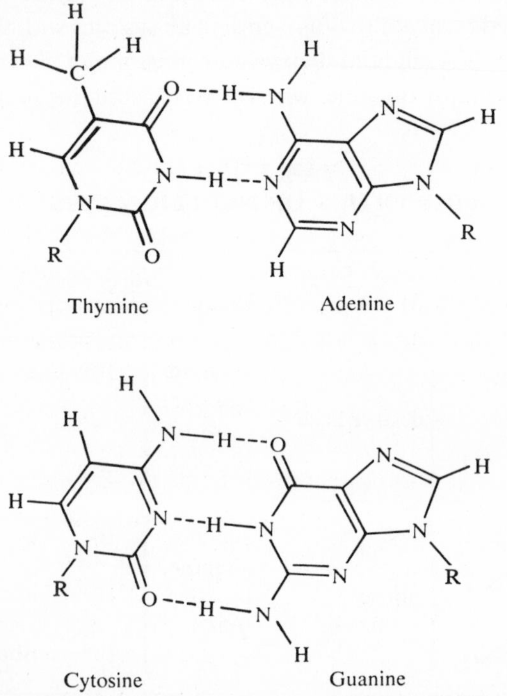

Thymine   Adenine

Cytosine   Guanine

Figure 11–3.   *Base pairs in DNA. R stands for the point of attachment of the nucleotide base to the deoxyribose of the backbone. Hydrogen bonds are shown as dashed lines.*

pairing. Note that in both cases a purine is paired with a pyrimidine.

From such base-pairing relationships it is clear that, if the sequence of one strand of the double helix be known, then the other may be predicted. If one strand may be said to convey certain information, the other obviously exists in a one-to-one mapping relationship to it, such that the operation of replacing each base by its complement would yield the original information. The only other comment that need be made here about DNA structure is to note that both single- and double-stranded DNA from a variety of sources appears to be circular—to contain no free ends. This conclusion has been reached from both genetic experiments with bacteria and viruses and electron-microscope observation of DNA from many sources, including mitochondria in higher animals. Circular DNA has not been observed in the nucleii of higher plants or animals. The reader is directed to the book by Watson listed in Suggested Reading for additional information about the structure and biology of nucleic acids.

The genetic code

It is worth considering what properties should be included in a code for the genetic description of cells, and, indeed, what sort of information needs to be provided. Two observations are central. In the first place, it is clear that cells are able to divide in such fashion that their genetic information is replicated. It is entirely possible for a cell and each of its billion (or so) progeny to have the same information content, so that cell replication must include concommitant information replication.

Furthermore, the synthesis of new cells requires information about a wide variety of cell attributes, having to do with all aspects of structure and physiology. There does, however, appear to be one central requirement, possibly underlying many of the others, and that is the requirement for complete information about the properties of the enzymes that the cell must make. The problem of the genetic code has thus been largely centered around the matter of enzyme synthesis, for the reason that the problem is encompassable (as these things go) and because there is a tacit assumption on the part of many that, if a cell is able to direct the synthesis of the right amount of the right kind of enzyme at the right time, everything else will necessarily follow. This assumption is considered at the end of the chapter.

In any case, it is true that the cell must be able to provide information for the synthesis of enzymes. To put it more explicitly, the cell must "know" the order of the 100 or more amino acids in a given protein and direct their placement in such a manner that no mistakes be made. There are essentially two ways in which this might be done, one being the formation of a protein from two half-proteins, the formation of the half-proteins from two halves, and so on, until two amino acids are put together. This sort of reverse chain-reaction mechanism is very probably untrue, as there is neither experimental evidence nor theoretical justification for it. A much more effective form of information transfer leading to protein synthesis and one for which there is impressive experimental evidence may be called the *template model* for protein synthesis. It states in effect that amino acids are lined up together on a template, or master plan, and that a protein is made as the result of a single process, with no intermediate "partial" proteins.

It is possible to say with some certainty that the template view is the correct one and that the template for protein formation is messenger RNA (or mRNA). Furthermore, it seems quite clear that messenger RNA is formed in the nucleus of cells and is a transcription, formed by base pairing, of the primary genetic code as located at the DNA molecule. Thus information of this kind is passed from generation to generation in the form of the sequence of bases in a DNA molecule, being replicated by means of base pairing. On the other hand, when the information is being made available to the protein-synthesizing apparatus, it is first transferred, again by base pairing, to a molecule of RNA, which serves as the template for lining up the amino acids.

This general scheme for information transfer appears to be valid as a description of protein synthesis, and we have detailed information about both the mechanisms for the synthesis and the intimate nature of the code. It develops that the code is quite similar to information storage in a man-made computing apparatus, with the message in the form of a linear sequence of symbols. While a computer uses a memory consisting of magnetic tape or a linearly arranged core, the memory of a cell consists of the arrangement of bases of the DNA molecule.

In the case of DNA, the symbols of the code are the individual nucleotide bases, and the words that they form are made up of groups of them. If one considers the task of DNA as specifying protein structure, it seems reasonable that a word should correspond to the location of a given amino acid in the protein chain.

Indeed, many of the words of the code are known. In all cases it appears that a word consists of a sequence of three bases, and the three together specify a single amino acid in a protein molecule. For example, if the term "uracil-uracil-uracil" appears in the text of a messenger RNA sequence, it specifies that the amino acid phenylalanine should appear at that point in the template. Similarly, "guanine-adenine-adenine" represents glutamic acid, and the meanings of many other triplets are known. The experimental basis for the cracking of the code forms as exciting a story as there is in biology, but unfortunately it is somewhat removed from the subject of this book. The reader is encouraged to see the book by Watson or the article by Ochoa listed in the Suggested Reading for additional information.

It is interesting to note that three bases make up a word and that there are four different bases (letters) in either DNA or RNA. This means that there are 4^3, or 64, different words possible to encode the 20 (or so) amino acids found in proteins. Note that two-letter words would be inadequate, leading only to 4^2, or 16, different words. It also develops that the code is degenerate, with more than one word representing a given amino acid. Finally, there appear to be words that do not mean anything at all, but represent a segment of "nonsense" when they appear, often as the result of a mutation.

"Reading out" the genetic code: protein synthesis

Just as a computer without a means of output is utterly useless, the biological code is meaningless unless it can transform the blueprint of a protein into the actual molecule with speed and accuracy. An error, such as a mutational error in the code itself or a mistake in transcription, will lead to an enzyme with one or more wrong amino acids, probably producing abnormal activity. The general pathway of *readout* of the genetic code was given above as passing from DNA to messenger RNA to protein. Further details are instructive.

The pathway of information transfer in protein synthesis is seen to occur in two steps, the first being the transcription of the DNA code into the base sequence of an RNA molecule. Then it remains to transform that information into the correct amino acid sequence of a protein. The first step might be described as the DNA-linked synthesis of messenger RNA and appears to take place in the nucleus of higher cells, where most of the DNA resides, As stated before, the information transfer takes place by base pairing, such that the DNA serves as template for the synthesis of the RNA. The actual synthesis involves the formation of covalent bonds between the bases, phosphate, and ribose, and an enzyme, termed RNA polymerase, manages this (noninformational) aspect. Clearly, since the sequence of bases in the RNA molecule was set up as a result of base pairing with those of the parent DNA, there should be a special relationship between the base contents of the DNA and the resultant RNA. In the simplest case, where the DNA template is single-stranded viral DNA, there is a very close correspondence between composition of the DNA and the complementary RNA such that, for example, the guanine content of the DNA equals the cytosine content of the RNA.

There is an additional form of specificity in the synthesis of messenger RNA. The cellular DNA is supposed to contain information for the synthesis of all the proteins a cell can make, but the cell does not necessarily form all those proteins at once. We have seen in Chapter 4 that many proteins are synthesized only when they are needed (only when an inducer is present). In this connection, it should be said that a given messenger RNA molecule contains information for the synthesis of a given protein, so that the decision as to which protein should be synthesized is made at the level of messenger RNA synthesis.

Thus a specific messenger RNA is formed at the nuclear DNA and serves, itself, as the template for a specific protein. Since the chief locus for protein synthesis is the ribosome, often located on the endoplasmic reticulum, it is clear that the messenger RNA must migrate from the nucleus into the cytoplasm. That done, the only remaining step is the translation of the code, still in the form of nucleotide base sequences, into an actual protein molecule. Since amino acids have been shown to have no special affinity for the template themselves, an additional step is necessary, which might be termed modification of the amino acid to enable it to find its place. The modification takes place in two steps, the first of which is often called *amino acid activation*, where an enzyme specific to each amino acid catalyzes the addition of an adenosine monophosphate unit to the amino acid:

$$\text{Amino acid} + \text{ATP} \longrightarrow \text{Amino acid-AMP} + \text{pyrophosphate}$$

Then, the same "activating enzyme" catalyzes the transfer of the amino acid to transfer RNA molecule, abbreviated tRNA*:

$$\text{Amino acid-AMP} + \text{tRNA} \longrightarrow \text{Amino acid-tRNA} + \text{AMP}$$

As in the case of the activating enzyme, there is a specific tRNA for each of the amino acids found in protein. As seen in Table 11–1, the

---

* Called soluble RNA (sRNA) by many writers.

tRNA molecule is small, with only about 80 or so bases, with some variation depending on which of the 20 tRNA molecules it is. It is interesting that all the tRNA's studied have the same terminal sequence at the end attached to the amino acid:

Amino acid-Adenine-Cytosine-Cytosine-

and that all have a greater or lesser proportion of bases which differ from the normal four found in RNA, of which examples are inosine and dihydrouridine.

The role of the tRNA is to enable the amino acid to seek the correct position on the mRNA template. The recognition occurs because a region of the tRNA molecule, consisting of three bases, bears a base sequence complementary to the three bases of the correct word of the mRNA code. This means that the problem of recognizing the amino acids is shifted to the activating enzyme (which brings the amino acid together with the appropriate tRNA) which, because of ordinary

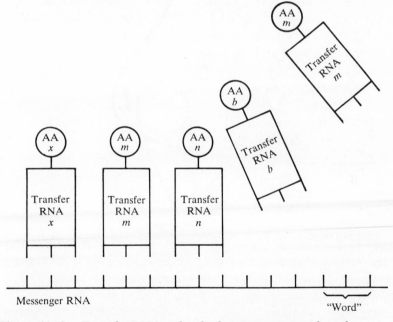

Figure 11–4. *Transfer RNA molecules bearing amino acids to the correct location on the messenger RNA template. Each transfer RNA molecule is specific to one amino acid and is bound at the correct location for that amino acid by hydrogen bonding between base pairs.*

enzyme specificity, is able to catalyze the reaction of the amino acid with the proper tRNA. The tRNA then lines up on the template (see Figure 11–4) and places the amino acid in the correct relation to the others, likewise lined up by means of their tRNA's. Thus the correct order of the amino acids is established, and the remaining problem is to synthesize the peptide bonds connecting them, certainly the simplest part of the whole procedure.

Although the activation of amino acids takes place in the soluble fraction of the cytoplasm (the part not easily sedimented), the actual synthesis of protein occurs largely at the ribosomes. This presents

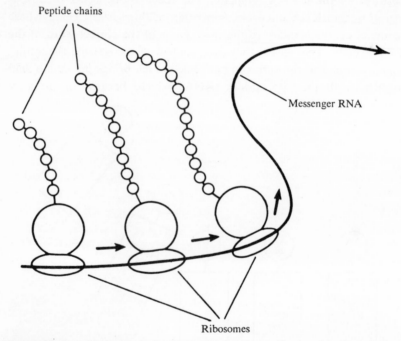

Figure 11–5. *The role of ribosomes in protein synthesis. A series of ribosomes is seen moving along the mRNA template, giving rise to increasingly long chains of amino acids. The ribosomes are seen to consist of two parts, differing in molecular weight by a factor of about two. Ribosomes dissociate under conditions of low Mg^{++} concentration to give the two subunits, which may be shown to be inactive in protein synthesis. The precise manner in which tRNA brings its appropriate amino acid into position for base pairing and peptide bond formation is not fully understood and is not depicted on this diagram.*

certain problems of a topological nature, as the template was said to be the linear chain of the mRNA molecule. An outline of how the ribosome is involved in scanning the template is given in Figure 11–5, where it is seen that the function of the ribosome is to allow the proper orientation of mRNA and tRNA-amino acids, so that peptide bond synthesis may occur. A number of ribosomes are seen to be scanning the same mRNA chain, a possibility deduced from the fact that ribosomes that are active in protein synthesis appear to be in the form of aggregates (polyribosomes), looking in electron micrographs rather like beads on a string. This simple view of protein synthesis obscures our many areas of ignorance, which include the details of the enzyme system responsible for peptide bond closure and the role of the large amount of ribosomal RNA, which appears to be quite without information content in the sense of specifying amino acid sequence. Note that, since no specificity for a given protein resides in the ribosomes, the same population of ribosomes may work toward the formation of different proteins, depending on what mRNA molecules may be about in the cytoplasm.

A property of mRNA that appears significant for regulation is its relatively short half-life in microorganisms. When the synthesis of mRNA specific to a given protein ceases, the free mRNA in the bacterial cytoplasm soon disappears, so that no more of that particular protein will be manufactured until new mRNA is formed at the DNA template. This transient character of mRNA is obviously suited to the rapid control of enzyme synthesis characteristic of microorganisms. In contrast, mRNA appears much more stable in cells of higher organisms, suggesting that, in such cases, different sorts of regulatory mechanisms must be in operation.

Regulation of protein synthesis

From our discussion of protein synthesis it should be clear that a crucial stage, from the point of view of regulation, must be the synthesis of the messenger RNA, specific to a given protein. Furthermore, from our prior consideration of enzyme synthesis, it was clear that regulation of protein synthesis does occur and must account both for the induction of enzyme formation and its repression. We saw in Chapter 5 that enzyme repression and induction were aspects of a single regulatory process. It now remains to describe that process in terms of the mechanism of protein synthesis.

Unfortunately, it is not yet possible to set down a final version of the repression (or induction) mechanism complete in all respects. It is possible, however, to present, in outline, features of the process which are probably quite valid. In the first place, it is believed (as we said earlier) that all regulation of enzyme synthesis takes place by means of repression. Induction is thus viewed as the removal of an internal repressor. Furthermore, repression seems to take place at the level of transcription of information between DNA and mRNA—by interfering with the synthesis of mRNA at the DNA template. Thus it has been shown that repression leads to a failure to make mRNA as well as protein.

It is naturally of interest to know the chemical identity of the repressor itself. Unfortunately, the repressor "substance" has not been isolated, a failure not difficult to understand in view of the very low concentrations that probably exist in cells. It does seem likely that repressors are proteins, a conclusion based on a number of items of circumstantial evidence, including the fact that the repressor itself appears to be under a genetic control similar to that governing protein synthesis. Thus the information needed for the synthesis of a repressor is encoded in the DNA genetic material as *regulatory genes* (as opposed to *structural genes* that provide information for ordinary protein formation). When such a regulatory gene is (—), the respective protein is not subject to repression, and the cell is constitutive with respect to it.

A description of the action of a repressor is not complete without a consideration of the role of such small molecules as the metabolic inducers and repressors described in Chapter 4. It begs the question to say that synthesis of a protein is under the control of another protein (the repressor) without any statement as to how *its* synthesis or activity is regulated. The theory of repression being advanced here, which is largely due to Jacob and Monod (see Suggested Reading) also involves interactions between the repressor and small molecules. According to the theory, the action of an inducer is to inactivate the repressor molecule. This is envisioned as occurring by means of binding of the inducer to the repressor protein, leading to a change in configuration. The repressor is quite analogous to an allosteric enzyme, as the binding of a small molecule at one site (the binding site for the inducer) leads to a change in activity at another site (that of the actual repression). A similar mechanism might explain the action of small molecules in preventing protein synthesis. Such molecules, which might be termed corepressors (by analogy with coenzymes), would also bind with the repressor protein and lead, this time, to an increase in repressor activity. Thus a repressor would seem to exist in active and inactive states, depending upon the nature of small molecules bound to it. These relationships are summarized in Figure 11–6.

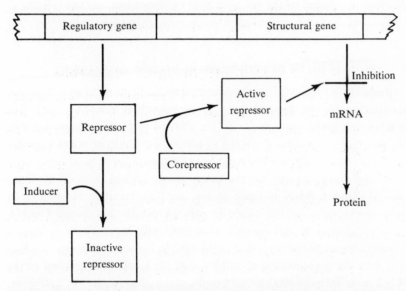

Figure 11–6. *Outline of regulation of protein synthesis. The regulatory (inducibility) gene is envisioned as providing information for the synthesis of a repressor molecule. This molecule would be activated by a co-repressor to inhibit protein synthesis at the nearby structural gene between that gene and its mRNA. The corepressor might be the end product of a metabolic pathway of which the protein catalyzed one reaction. Failure of the regulatory gene to give rise to the repressor molecule would result in the constitutive synthesis of the protein. The role of an inducer would be to inactivate the repressor molecule, leading to unimpaired protein synthesis.*

An additional advantage of the repressor-linked control of enzyme synthesis is that a number of proteins could well be under the control of one repressor. It is often true that closely related enzymes have genetic loci quite closely linked on the DNA map. It appears that in such cases adjacent loci can together serve as template for the synthesis of a single mRNA molecule, which would thus carry information for the formation of several closely related enzymes. Since a single repressor would regulate the transcription of the whole mRNA molecule, the whole series of enzymes would be under a single mode of control. This appears important in instances where several enzymes of a metabolic pathway are repressed by the buildup of a single final product. For a more detailed discussion of the phenomenon of repression, see the references to Watson or Jacob and Monod given in Suggested Reading.

Control of protein synthesis in higher organisms

Regulation of protein synthesis in microorganisms must be considered in relation to the extreme liability of microbial mRNA. Since free mRNA is rapidly broken down, the control of protein formation can reside in the regulation of mRNA synthesis. Cessation of mRNA formation will thus rapidly lead to complete elimination of protein formation.

In higher organisms, on the other hand, several lines of evidence indicate that mRNA is quite stable, so that sensitive regulation of protein synthesis cannot reside in mRNA production alone. Clearly, such regulation would involve excessive time lags. There is now a growing body of evidence that regulation in higher organisms is subsequent to the manufacture of mRNA—at the level of translation of the RNA code into the final protein molecule. For example, the antibiotic, actinomycin D, inhibits mRNA formation but under certain conditions, fails to prevent protein synthesis. In these circumstances protein synthesis must be imagined to occur by means of extant, and relatively stable, mRNA. Such protein synthesis in the absence of new mRNA synthesis appears subject to regulation of an inductive nature, including stimulation by hormones in suitable tissue. This regulation can only occur at a site subsequent to mRNA production—the "reading out" of the code represented by the mRNA molecule. There is evidence that the mechanism for such regulation involves the masking of the mRNA code by a protein coat and that stimulation of activity results from the removal of the mask, but sufficient information about such matters is not yet available.

The adequacy of the genetic code

The view of information transfer in protein synthesis outlined above appears to explain much of what is known about enzyme formation in cells. Although many details remain to be worked out, it seems increasingly unlikely that the general outline will prove invalid. There appears ample justification for the statement that DNA bears information required for the ordering of amino acids in proteins and that information transfer is by means of the special relationships that exist due to the geometry of nucleotide bases. It is thus tempting to argue that DNA is *the* genetic material—that it carries all information required for the synthesis of cells—and many biologists appear prepared to make this assertion. It is one thing, however, to say that information transfer and storage take place as we have described them; it is quite another to say that there are no other paths for such transfer. The world of the cell is exceedingly rich in phenomena, all of which might be said to require some sort of information transfer for their continuance. The question is whether or not the Spartan mechanism of information transfer through DNA and mRNA to protein is sufficient to provide for the richness and complexity of cells.

For example, consider the matter of location of apparatus for making proteins. The preceding description places protein synthesis at the ribosomes and views information as passing from the nuclear DNA to the cytoplasmic ribosome. In fact, this pattern appears untrue for a portion of total cellular protein synthesis—that associated with closed organelles such as chloroplasts or mitochondria. For example, protein synthesis *within* mitochondria is known to occur, and it is likely that the information for it is encoded in a separate mitochondrial DNA which has been demonstrated both chemically and by means of electron microscopy. Similar observations have been made using chloroplasts. It is interesting that mitochondrial DNA molecules appear to be circular, with no free ends, a property they share with DNA from a number of bacteria and viruses, seen again by electron microscopy as well as by genetic mapping.

The observation of genetic material in the form of DNA closely associated with cell organelles should not be surprising in view of the indications that mitochondria and chloroplasts (as well as other organelles) possess a degree of genetic autonomy. For example, Euglena chloroplasts appear to be self-replicating, and it is possible to "cure" the cells of them, after which no more may be made. There is also considerable evidence that yeast mitochondria are at least partially responsible for their own formation, a view supported by the subsequent observation of mitochondrial DNA. Such autonomy should also not be totally unexpected, in view of the obvious problems in imagining that ribosomal protein synthesis could be the means for the formation of enzyme molecules *within* a closed mitochondrial membrane, or those comprising that membrane. Thus there may be more than one pathway for information transfer within cells, just as there appear to be sites of information storage in the form of extranuclear DNA.

Finally, one should probably maintain an open mind as to the possibility of cellular information storage and transfer not involving DNA. At the present time it appears likely that protein synthesis proceeds from information encoded in DNA, and the basic assumption of molecular biology that information transfer is one-way—that protein cannot serve as a template for nucleic acid synthesis—is valid. A second assumption should be considered with some care—the widely held view that the only genetic information necessary for the production of a new cell is that required for the production of the right amount of the right proteins (enzymes). In other words (putting it rather crudely), if one could make all the right enzymes, the cell would flop together, owing to the intermolecular forces between the various components. This approach may be correct, but there is little basis at the present time to enable one to support or reject it. It is also possible that the total information content of the cell is more than that of the individual enzymes and that its storage and transfer from one generation to the next is of an order of complexity greater than the DNA code for amino acid sequence in proteins. It may be that the spatial interrelationship between different enzymes, such as those comprising the cellular membranes, is of great significance in determining function and must be provided for in the total information available at the time of division. The three-dimensional morphology of cells must also be explained eventually in terms of genetics, and the state of the art is still such that an open mind is beneficial. For example, it might be (and has been) argued that the genetic information available to a new cell at the time of division includes not only the DNA code but is encoded also in the totality of the structure of the cell. To give a simple example, the information that enables cells to have mitochondria outside (rather than inside) the nuclear membrane might be thought to be encoded in the fact that, in the parent cell, the mitochondria *are* outside (in the cytoplasm). When similar arguments are advanced to explain the determination of other aspects of cell morphology, the statements often made about cells being autocatalytic (see Chapter 10) take on somewhat richer meaning, with the totality of a cell presiding at the formation of its progeny. In any case, the cell biologist should be conditioned to look for genetic determinants appropriate to the beauty and complexity that it is his privilege to find in the living cell.

Suggested Reading

CHANTRENNE, H., *The Biosynthesis of Proteins*, Pergamon Press, Oxford, 1961.

COHEN, N. R., "The control of protein biosynthesis," *Biol. Rev.*, **41**, 503 (1966).

JACOB, F., and J. MONOD, "Genetic regulatory mechanisms in the synthesis of proteins," *J. Mol. Biol.*, **3**, 318 (1961).

OCHOA, S., "Synthetic polynucleotides and the genetic code," in *Informational Macromolecules*, H. J. Vogel, V. Bryson, and J. O. Lampen (eds.), Academic Press, New York, 1963.

STAHL, F. W., *The Mechanics of Inheritance*, Prentice-Hall, Englewood Cliffs, N.J., 1964.

WATSON, J. D., *The Molecular Biology of the Gene*, W. A. Benjamin, New York, 1965.

Suggested Reading

Index

211